# LONGMAN
# SCIENCE

D1373117

# TEACHER'S GUIDE

Longman

# Longman Science Teacher's Guide

Thanks to Charles Green for his contribution.

Copyright © 2006 by Pearson Education, Inc.
All rights reserved.

No part of this publication may be reproduced,
stored in a retrieval system, or transmitted
in any form or by any means, electronic, mechanical,
photocopying, recording, or otherwise,
without the prior permission of the publisher,
with the exception of pages 187–238,
which may be duplicated for classroom use.

Pearson Education, 10 Bank Street, White Plains, NY 10606

Vice president, primary and secondary editorial: Ed Lamprich
Senior development editors: Lauren Weidenman and Virginia Bernard
Development editor: Deborah Maya Lazarus
Editorial coordinator: Johnnie Farmer
Editorial assistant: Emily Lippincott
Vice president, director of production and design: Rhea Banker
Production supervisor: Christine Edmonds
Production editor: Laurie Neaman
Vice president, marketing: Kate McLoughlin
Senior marketing manager: Don Wulbrecht
Senior manufacturing buyer: Nancy Flaggman
Cover design: Rhea Banker
Text design and composition: Quarasan
Text font: 11.5/15 Minion Regular
Credits: See page 241.

## LONGMAN ON THE WEB

**Longman.com** offers online resources for teachers and students. Access our Companion Websites, our online catalog, and our local offices around the world.

Visit us at **longman.com**.

ISBN: 0-13-193032-X

Printed in the United States of America
1 2 3 4 5 6 7 8 9 10–CRK–09 08 07 06 05

# Contents

# Scope and Sequence

| | | Science Skills | | Experiment |
|---|---|---|---|---|
| | | **Reading Strategies** | **Using Visuals** | |
| **Getting Started** | Introduction | Preview and predict | Introduction to visuals | Observe water movement in a flower |
| **Unit 1 Plants** | Lesson 1 | Main idea and details | Diagrams | Grow a plant |
| | Lesson 2 | Compare and contrast | Cycle diagrams | |
| **Unit 2 Animals** | Lesson 1 | Use what you know | Photographs | Compare animal traits |
| | Lesson 2 | Key sentences | Pie chart | |
| **Unit 3 Rocks and Minerals** | Lesson 1 | Ask questions | Sectional diagrams | Make models of rocks |
| | Lesson 2 | Cause and effect | Photo sequences | |
| **Unit 4 Planets and Stars** | Lesson 1 | Reread | Illustrations | Make a model of our solar system |
| | Lesson 2 | Visualize | Deep space photos | |
| **Unit 5 Matter** | Lesson 1 | Facts and examples | Micrographs | Observe density |
| | Lesson 2 | Idea maps | States of matter illustrations | |
| **Unit 6 Sound and Light** | Lesson 1 | Act it out | Charts | Observe light |
| | Lesson 2 | Draw a picture | Wave diagrams | |

# Program Overview

*Longman Science* is a program for English Language Learners (ELLs) and struggling readers who need to learn science concepts and vocabulary. It is designed for students at the beginning level of English proficiency. The program aims to help students learn key science vocabulary, understand science terms and concepts, acquire and practice reading strategies, understand and use visuals, and develop essential academic language. Students will finish this course equipped with the vocabulary and skills needed to succeed in mainstream science classes.

The *Longman Science* program integrates the following best practices for teaching English Language Learners.

- **Scaffolding** Point-of-use scaffolding is provided to make the language of content material more meaningful to beginning students. Science content is scaffolded through the restatement of key concepts in simplified language, and the use of photographs, diagrams, charts, illustrations, and graphic organizers.

- **Graphic Organizers** Graphic organizers provide a visual representation of information for strategies such as main idea and details, cause and effect, compare and contrast, facts and examples, and idea mapping to help students grasp the skills and information they need to learn.

- **Academic Language** Understanding the academic language used in the classroom, in textbooks, and on standardized tests is vital to the success of English Language Learners. *Longman Science* makes this academic language explicit through the teaching of science skills.

- **Science Skills** Reading for content knowledge and understanding how to use visuals are important skills for students to master in order to succeed in content area classes. *Longman Science* introduces and provides practice of a different reading strategy in each lesson. It also provides practice in using a wide range of visuals that students will encounter in mainstream science textbooks.

Skills are introduced at the beginning of each lesson, practiced throughout the reading, and assessed at the end of each lesson and in the unit review.

## Components

*Longman Science* consists of a Student Book, a Workbook, and a Teacher's Guide.

### Student Book

The Getting Started unit introduces students to the field of science, including the scientific method, and to visuals such as photographs, diagrams, illustrations, and charts. The six units that follow provide a broad overview of science themes generally taught in middle and high school science classes.

Each unit consists of three parts: Lesson 1, Lesson 2, and a Unit Review. Each lesson includes key vocabulary, a reading strategy, a focus on using visuals, a content reading, and a review and practice section. Each unit ends with a hands-on experiment.

To make science engaging and relevant, all content readings include the following features:

- **Science at Home** boxes offer a simple activity related to the lesson for students to investigate on their own, at home or in their community.

- **Science Now** boxes inform students of a recent discovery, technological advance, or trend in science related to the topic of the unit.

- **Environment Watch** boxes highlight an environmental issue related to the unit topic. Examples of issues include deforestation and glacial melting.

- **Curriculum Connection** boxes offer information related to the lesson but originating in other disciplines such as history, math, art, and music.

- **Language Tip** boxes explain or illustrate a new point of grammar or word study appearing in the reading text on that page.

- **As You Read** boxes encourage students to practice the lesson's reading strategy.
- **Leaders in Science** boxes spotlight an important scientist whose work relates to the topic of the unit.
- **Exploring** pages explore in more depth a key point of interest related to the unit topic.
- **Before You Go On** questions provide an ongoing comprehension check that asks students to recall, understand, and interpret information presented on each two-page spread.

The Student Book also includes:
- a **Review and Practice** section after each lesson to check that students have learned the important elements of the lesson.
- an **Experiment** section at the end of each unit that utilizes the steps of the scientific method to do hands-on experiments.
- a **Glossary** that provides an extensive list of content vocabulary, definitions, and pronunciation for students' reference.

## Workbook

The Workbook provides exercises and critical thinking activities to extend practice of key vocabulary, science skills, unit concepts, and writing. Workbook activities correspond to each section of the lesson and are indicated with a corresponding icon on the Student Book pages. The Workbook also includes an Experiment Log to record information while doing the unit experiments.

## Teacher's Guide

The Teacher's Guide provides complete point-of-use instructions for each lesson in the Student Book. This instructions include guidelines for:
- addressing different learning modalities
- demonstrating concepts
- providing direct instruction
- teaching and modeling reading strategies
- using graphic organizers
- using visuals

The first page of each Teacher's Guide unit begins with an overview of the unit contents, reading strategies, featured visuals, experiment, and learning objectives. The pages that follow provide direct instructional suggestions and procedures to present and teach key vocabulary, science skills, and content.

The Teacher's Guide uses a two-phase approach for teaching each reading section:
- **Preview Pages** using effective techniques for English Language Learners.
- **Teach Pages** using reading strategies, comprehension checks, and graphic organizers to help students understand, organize, and synthesize new concepts. Teachers can introduce the additional boxed material on the page whenever they feel it is appropriate. The answers to the Before You Go On questions are also in this section.

The Teacher's Guide provides the following additional support:
- **Reaching All Students** activities that give specific suggestions on adapting the content and reading strategies to auditory, visual, and/or kinesthetic learners.
- **Optional Activities** that enhance or extend the topic.
- **Website** prompts that direct students to links to interesting sites.

The Teacher's Guide also includes:
- a Scope and Sequence chart
- Student Book Answers
- Workbook Answer Key
- Tests
- Tests Answer Key

# Optional Vocabulary Activities

The Student Book and Workbook contain a variety of exercises to help students practice the key vocabulary words that are introduced in each unit. However, reinforcing vocabulary with games and other activities is a fun way to help students learn. Here are some activities to adapt to your classroom. They can be used for practicing any content vocabulary from *Longman Science*.

## 1. Grab and Run
### Visual and kinesthetic learners
List the vocabulary words on index cards, one word per card, and attach them to the board, randomly or in columns and rows. Divide the class into two or three teams. The first member of each team runs to the board as you read a definition. The first one to find the correct word grabs it and returns to his or her seat. Then the next team members repeat the same process with your next definition. The team with the most captured words at the end of the game wins.

## 2. Word and Number Bingo
### Visual and auditory learners
Give out blank bingo cards or tell students to make their own. Have students fill in numbers from 1 to 20 randomly on their cards. Write the vocabulary words on the board, assigning a number to each one. Have the definitions previously written on slips of paper, which you withdraw from a bag and read. Students will need to look for the correct word on the board and cover the corresponding number on their bingo cards. The usual rules for winning bingo apply.

## 3. What Are You?
### Auditory learners
Write the vocabulary words on index cards and put them in a bag. Have a volunteer pick a card, look at it, and show it to you. Then students take turns asking the volunteer yes-no questions to ascertain the word. Questions should be in the form of, *Are you . . . ? Do you . . . ?* Students will only be able to ask ten questions. The student who guesses the target word becomes the next volunteer.

## 4. Pick a Task, Pick a Word
### Visual, auditory, and kinesthetic learners
You will need two envelopes to prepare for this game. In one envelope, place all the vocabulary words on individual slips of paper. In the second envelope, write these four choices on individual slips: *define the word, pronounce the word, create a sentence,* and *spell the word.* Divide the class into two teams. One student from one of the teams comes to the front of the class and draws a piece of paper from the second envelope containing the four choices. If the student picked *pronounce the word, create a sentence,* or *define the word,* then he or she picks a word from the first envelope and does what was indicated by his/her choice. If the student picked *spell the word,* he or she picks a word from the first envelope and immediately passes the chosen slip of paper to you without looking at it. You say the word and the student must spell it. If the student does the task correctly without help from teammates, that team gets 3 points. If the team helps, it gets 1 point.

## 5. Tic-Tac-Toe
### Visual and kinesthetic learners
Make a tic-tac-toe grid on the board with nine of the vocabulary words listed on it. Divide the class into two teams (X and O). The first team chooses a word from the grid and gives a sentence using that word. If the sentence is correct, that team can put its mark in that box. The first team to get three Xs or Os in a row is the winner. Tic-tac-toe can also be played at students' desks in pairs. Another variation is to have students give the definition instead of a sentence.

## 6. Memory Match
### Visual and kinesthetic learners
Have pairs of students write each vocabulary word on one half of an index card and its definition on the other half. Cut the cards in half to make the game. Shuffle the cards and turn them over, arranging them randomly. Students take turns turning over two cards and reading what they say. If both cards are vocabulary words or definitions, the student reads them and turns them over again. If one card has a definition and the other card has a vocabulary word, the student decides if they match. If they match, the student keeps the cards. Whoever has the most matches at the end of the game is the winner.

## 7. Throw the Dice
### Visual and kinesthetic learners
Write twelve vocabulary words on the board, numbering them from 1 to 12. Divide students into pairs or groups of three. Give each group a pair of dice. The first student rolls the dice and looks for the number on the board that he or she has rolled. The first time the student rolls that number, he or she pronounces the word next to that number. If the student happens to roll the same number again later on, he or she defines the word. If the student rolls that number a third time, he or she makes a sentence with that word. Students earn 1 point for pronouncing the word, 2 points for defining it, and 3 points for making a reasonable sentence. Set a time limit for the game. The student with the most points is the winner.

## 8. Word Association
### Auditory, visual, and kinesthetic learners
Prepare a list of target vocabulary words. Then prepare a different list of words associated with the various vocabulary words. Make sure you have several related words for each vocabulary item. Write one of your target vocabulary words on the board. Select someone to be the scorekeeper. Tell students they are going to listen to a list of words that you will read slowly. When they hear a word that is associated with the vocabulary word on the board, they should immediately raise their hands. The first one to raise his or her hand gets a point, which the scorekeeper will record. Other students may challenge the one who raised a hand to explain the association. Quicken the pace of the game and repeat words to keep students interested and the game lively. A variation would be to have students silently write the words down instead of raising their hands.

## 9. Chart the Parts of Speech
### Visual and kinesthetic learners
Have students make a chart in their notebooks with three column headings: *Noun, Verb,* and *Adjective.* At the end of one or more units, have students categorize their key vocabulary words under the correct part(s) of speech. Some words may fall into more than one category, or there may be related forms of the word that you want students to include.

## 10. Content Word Wall
### Visual learners
Make a Word Wall of large-lettered words displayed on mural or poster paper. As students progress through the units, ask them what words they would like to place on the classroom Word Wall. Make the Word Wall interactive by incorporating those words into other listening, speaking, reading, and writing activities. Use them in dictated sentences, hangman games, crossword puzzles, bingo, categorizing, tic-tac-toe, chants, and word searches.

# Introduction
## Getting Started Overview

| Content | Science Skills | | Experiment |
| --- | --- | --- | --- |
| | **Reading Strategies** | **Using Visuals** | |
| • What Is Science?<br>• The Sciences<br>• Meet a Scientist<br>• The Scientific Method<br>• Safety<br>• Practicing the Scientific Method<br>• Science Tools<br>• Visuals<br>• Science Reading Strategies | Preview<br>Predict | Overview | How Does Water Move inside a Flower? |

## Objectives

### Vocabulary
- Develop new vocabulary related to science
- Use newly acquired vocabulary in context

### Concepts
- Learn the definition of life, earth, and physical sciences
- Learn about the scientific method
- Learn about science tools and classroom safety

### Reading Strategies
- Preview to understand what you read
- Predict to understand what you read

### Using Visuals
- Become familiar with the visuals used in the book

### Experiment
- Practice the scientific method

# What Is Science?, page 2
# The Sciences, pages 3–5
## Life Science, page 3

## Preview Pages

Introduce students to *Longman Science* by starting with the cover. Have pairs of students say whatever they can about the cover in a few minutes. Then as a class, identify the pictures, naming everything in English but allowing students to use their native languages if they need to. Read the title and tell students, *You are going to learn about different kinds of science.*

Turn to pages 2 and 3. Hold up your book, point to the headings, and ask students, *What does this say?* Call on individual students to answer. Point to each picture and say, *Look at this picture. Look at the caption.* Read each caption aloud as students follow along in their books. Make sure students are looking at the correct picture and caption. (The preview strategy will be formally presented at the end of this unit, so this is really just a warm-up to get students used to following the strategy.) Keep vocabulary explanations to a minimum for now.

## Teach Pages

Read the text aloud, or call on individual students to read it. Use pictures, drawings on the board, and mime to teach the meaning of new words. Help students with pronunciation.

Have students read the pages again to themselves. Alternatively, have pairs or small groups of students read aloud to each other.

**Understand Information** Ask comprehension and picture questions. Depending on students' abilities, you may want to ask more *yes-no* questions than *Wh-* questions. If helpful, write all or part of each question and answer on the board; alternatively, model the question and the type of response you expect.

Hold up your book as you ask questions such as (pointing to the picture of the koala; then pointing to the caption), *Is this a plant or an animal? What animal is it? Do scientists study animals?* (pointing to the earth) *Is this a planet? What is its name? Do you live here? Do scientists study the planet Earth?* (pointing to the ice) *Do scientists study matter? Is this matter? What kind of matter is it?* (pointing to the text on page 2; point to individual sentences, if helpful) *What is science the study of? Is it the study of the earth and planets? What else is it the study of? What do scientists do? Do they ask questions? What else do they do?* (pointing to the text on page 3) *Do scientists study only one kind of science? What's one kind of science you'll learn about? What's another? What is life science the study of?* Continue asking similar questions about all the pictures and the text.

**Organize Information** Write *paragraph* on the board. Point to the second paragraph on page 3 and say, *This is a paragraph. A paragraph is a group of sentences.* Write *Make a chart* on the board. Say, *Let's make a chart about this paragraph.*

Draw a chart on the board. Ask (pointing to the heading, if helpful), *What is this paragraph about?* Write *Life Science* at the top of the chart. Have students copy the chart into their notebooks. Say, *Look at the paragraph. What is life science? What are living things? What else are living things?* Write the responses in the chart and have students copy them into their notebooks. Write *understand* and *remember* on the board. Say, *This chart will help us understand life science. It will also help us remember.* The chart might look like this:

| Life Science |
| --- |
| Life science is the study of living things on Earth. Animals are living things. Plants are also living things. |

 Workbook page 1 may now be assigned for homework or done in class. Make sure that students understand how to complete the workbook page by reading the directions with the class first. Go over the task on the page before students begin. Elicit the first few answers for each exercise.

## Earth Science, page 4
## Physical Science, page 5

### Preview Pages

Hold up your book, point to the headings, and ask students, *What does this say?* Call on individual students to answer. Point to each picture and say, *Look at this picture. Look at the caption.* Read each caption aloud as students follow along in their books. Make sure students are looking at the correct picture and caption. Keep vocabulary explanations to a minimum for now.

### Teach Pages

Read the text aloud, or call on individual students to read it. Use pictures, drawings on the board, and mime to teach the meaning of new words. Help students with pronunciation.

Have students read the pages again to themselves. Alternatively, have pairs or small groups of students read aloud to each other.

**Understand Information** Ask comprehension and picture questions. Depending on students' abilities, you may want to ask more *yes-no* questions than *Wh-* questions. If helpful, write all or part of each question and answer on the board; alternatively, repeat the question and verbally model the type of response you expect.

Hold up your book as you ask questions such as (pointing to the picture of scientists standing on cool solid rock), *Who are these people? What are they doing? What are they standing on? Is one man wearing a mask covering his face? Why? What is the orange-red liquid?* (pointing to the water in the beach scene) *What is this?* (pointing to the air) *What is this?* (pointing to the land) *What is this? What makes up Earth's environment?* (pointing to Saturn) *Is this a planet? What planet is it? Is it near Earth?* (pointing to the text on page 4) *What is earth science the study of? Is it the study of the environment? What is the environment? Is it the study of rock? What kind of rock? What kind of rock is our earth made of?* (pointing to the picture of electricity) *What is this? What color is the electricity? What is a type of energy?* (pointing to the girl on the horse) *Is she matter? Is this horse matter?* Continue asking similar questions about all the pictures and the text.

**Organize Information** Say, *Let's make a chart about these paragraphs.* Draw a chart on the board. Ask (pointing to the heading on page 4, if helpful), *What are these paragraphs about?* Write *Earth Science* at the top of the chart. Have students copy the chart into their notebooks. Say, *Look at the paragraphs. What is earth science?* Write two responses in the chart and have students copy them into their notebooks. Ask, *What else is it the study of?* Elicit the answer verbally, but don't write it on the board. Have students finish the chart in pairs. After students have completed their charts, elicit the information for the rest of the chart and write it on the board. The chart might look like this:

| Earth Science |
| --- |
| Earth science is the study of the earth.<br>It is the study of the environment.<br>It is the study of hot and cool rock.<br>Earth science is the study of the sun.<br>It is the study of the stars.<br>It is also the study of other planets. |

Follow the same procedure for making a chart about physical science. Then write *understand* and *remember* on the board. Say, *This chart will help us understand physical science. It will also help us remember.*

## REACHING ALL STUDENTS: Visual Learners

Have students make a picture dictionary of highly visual words on these pages. Ask, *What is earth science?* (It is the study of the earth.) Write the word *Earth* on the board. Say, *Now I can draw a picture of the earth. Draw a simple Earth.* Say, *Write* Earth *in your notebook. Draw a picture of Earth.* Write some or all of the following words on the board: *sun, stars, book, rock, water, electricity.* Have students draw their own pictures in their notebooks. Later, have students show their pictures to the class.

## Before You Go On

Do this exercise together as a class. Read aloud or have a student read aloud the first question and have the class write it in their notebooks. Ask students to look at the text. Have them find and read the sentence that answers the question. Help them craft an answer to the question. Ask, *How can I answer the question: What is the environment? I need to say: The environment is . . .* Write this phrase on the board and elicit the conclusion. Have students copy the answer in their notebooks. Complete the other questions in the same manner.

**Answers**
1. The environment is the land, oceans, and air on the earth.
2. Some examples of matter are a book, rocks, and water. They are nonliving matter.
3. Some examples of energy are electricity, sound, and light.

 Workbook pages 2–4 may now be assigned for homework or done in class. Make sure that students understand how to complete the workbook pages by reading the directions with the class first. Go over the task on the page before students begin. Elicit the first few answers for each exercise.

## Meet a Scientist, pages 6–7

### Preview Pages

Hold up your book, point to the headings, and ask students, *What does this say?* Call on individual students to answer. Point to each picture and say, *Look at this picture. Look at the caption.* Read each caption aloud as students follow along in their books. Make sure students are looking at the correct picture and caption. Keep vocabulary explanations to a minimum for now.

### Teach Pages

Read the text aloud, or call on individual students to read it. Use pictures, drawings on the board, and mime to teach the meaning of new words. Help students with pronunciation.

Have students read the pages again to themselves. Alternatively, have pairs or small groups of students read aloud to each other.

**Understand Information** Ask comprehension and picture questions. Depending on students' abilities, you may want to ask more *yes-no* questions than *Wh-*questions. If helpful, write all or part of each question and answer on the board; alternatively, repeat the question and verbally model the type of response you expect.

Hold up your book as you ask questions such as (pointing to Dian Fossey), *Who is this woman? What was she?* (pointing to the gorilla) *What is this? How much can mountain gorillas weigh?* (pointing to the text on page 6) *Did Dian Fossey study gorillas? Where did she study the mountain gorillas? What did she want to learn? How long did Fossey watch the gorillas?* Continue asking similar questions about all the pictures and the text.

**Organize Information** Write *Make a word web* on the board. Say, *Let's make a word web about Dian Fossey.* Draw a circle on the board labeled *Dian Fossey.* Ask, pointing to the first paragraph on page 6, *Who was Dian Fossey?* Write *scientist* in another circle extending off from the first one. Ask, *What did she study?* Elicit *mountain gorillas* and write it on the board. Ask questions and model finishing the web on the board. Have students copy the web into their notebooks. Pair students and have them tell each other about Dian Fossey in their own words, using the information on the web. The web might look like this:

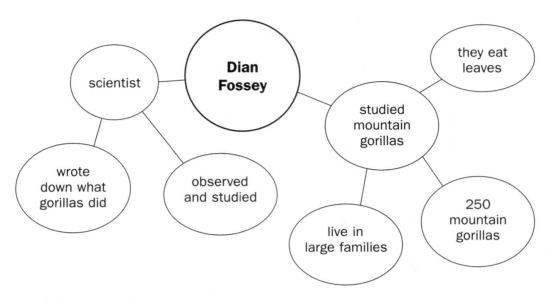

# The Scientific Method, pages 8–13
## Asking Questions, page 9

### Preview Pages

Hold up your book, point to the headings, and ask students, *What does this say?* Call on individual students to answer. Point to each picture and say, *Look at this picture. Look at the caption.* Make sure students are looking at the correct picture and caption. Keep vocabulary explanations to a minimum for now.

### Teach Pages

Read the text aloud, or call on individual students to read it. Use pictures, drawings on the board, and mime to teach the meaning of new words. Help students with pronunciation.

Have students read the pages again to themselves. Alternatively, have pairs or small groups of students read aloud to each other.

**Understand Information** Ask comprehension and picture questions. Depending on students' abilities, you may want to ask more *yes-no* questions than *Wh-* questions. If helpful, write all or part of each question and answer on the board; alternatively, repeat the question and verbally model the type of response you expect.

Hold up your book as you ask questions such as (pointing to the text on page 8), *What do scientists want to find out? What do they do with the information? What do they want to show others? Do scientists use the scientific method? How many steps are in the scientific method? What are they?* Continue asking similar questions about all the pictures and the text.

**Organize Information** Say, *Let's make a chart.* Draw a chart on the board with two columns. Ask, *What is step 1 of the scientific method?* Point to the relevant part of the text, if helpful. Write the response in the chart. Ask, *What does "asking questions" mean?* Write the response on the board. Say, *Let's give an example. What is an example of asking questions?* Elicit an example and write it on the board. Have students copy the chart so far. Explain that they will add more later. The beginning chart might look like this:

| Step 1: Asking Questions | Example |
|---|---|
| Scientists ask questions about the world. | What do seeds need to grow? |

## REACHING ALL STUDENTS: Visual and Kinesthetic Learners

Bring a few different seeds to class along with pictures of what the plants look like from seed packets or the Internet. Write the names of the plants on the board. Have students draw a labeled picture of the seed and the plant in their notebooks.

### Before You Go On

Do this exercise together as a class. Read or have a student read the first question, and have the class write it in their notebooks. Model the activity by writing the question on the board. Ask students to look at the text. Have them find and read the sentence that answers the question. Write the answer on the board and have students copy it into their notebooks. Complete the other questions in the same manner.

**Answers**
1. Scientists use the scientific method to show their ideas are correct.
2. The five steps of the scientific method are (1) asking questions, (2) making a hypothesis, (3) testing the hypothesis, (4) observing, and (5) drawing conclusions.
3. You ask, "What do seeds need to grow?"

## Making a Hypothesis, page 10
## Testing the Hypothesis, page 11
## Observing, page 11

Making a Hypothesis, page 10
Testing the Hypothesis, page 11
Observing, page 11

### Preview Pages

Hold up your book, point to the headings, and ask students, *What does this say?* Call on individual students to answer. Point to each picture and say, *Look at this picture. Look at the caption.* Read each caption aloud as students follow along in their books. Make sure students are looking at the correct picture and caption. Keep vocabulary explanations to a minimum for now.

### Teach Pages

Read the text aloud, or call on individual students to read it. Use pictures, drawings on the board, and mime to teach the meaning of new words. Help students with pronunciation.

Have students read the pages again to themselves. Alternatively, have pairs or small groups of students read aloud to each other.

**Understand Information**   Ask comprehension and picture questions. Depending on students' abilities, you may want to ask more *yes-no* questions than *Wh-* questions. If helpful, write all or part of each question and answer on the board; alternatively, repeat the question and verbally model the type of response you expect.

Hold up your book as you ask questions such as, *What do scientists do after asking a question? What is this called? What do you do next? What do you think? Do scientists test their hypothesis after they make it? What do they find out? What's a good way to test a hypothesis? How do you test your hypothesis about seeds?* Continue asking similar questions about all the pictures and text.

**Organize Information**   Draw a chart on the board with two columns. Ask, *What is step 2 of the scientific method?* Point to the relevant part of the text, if helpful. Write the response in the chart. Ask, *What is making a hypothesis?* Write the response on the board. Say, *Let's give an example. What is an example of making a hypothesis?* Elicit a sentence and write it on the board. Have students add this information to the chart they started for step 1. Then continue the chart on the board. Ask, *What's step 3? What's step 4?* Write the responses in the chart. Have students work in pairs, in small groups, or individually to complete examples for these steps. Circulate to monitor and help students. Check answers together as a class. The chart might look like this:

| Step 1: Asking Questions | Example |
|---|---|
| Scientists ask questions about the world. | What do seeds need to grow? |
| **Step 2: Making a Hypothesis** | **Example** |
| Scientists try to guess the answer to their question. | The seeds need water to grow. |
| **Step 3: Testing the Hypothesis** | **Example** |
| Scientists find out if their idea is correct. Doing an experiment is a good way to test a hypothesis. | You put a paper towel and a bean in a jar. Then you add water. |
| **Step 4: Observing** | **Example** |
| Scientists observe, or watch very carefully. Scientists look, listen, touch, and think. | You observe the bean take in water and get bigger. Then you observe the bean growing into a plant. |

## Before You Go On

Do this exercise together as a class. Read or have a student read the first question, and have the class write it in their notebooks. Model the activity on the board. Ask students to look at the text. Have them find and read the sentence that answers the first question. Write the answer on the board and have students copy it into their notebooks. Complete the other questions in the same manner.

### Answers
1. After scientists make a hypothesis, they test it.
2. A good way to test a hypothesis is to do an experiment.
3. Scientists observe very carefully. They look, listen, touch, and think.

## Optional Activity

Bring one or more jars, beans or seeds, paper towels, and water to class. Perform or have students perform the experiment on these pages. After seeds have germinated, plant or have students plant them in soil and water them. This will allow students to see concepts from Unit 1, Lesson 1 in action. It may also provide you with plants to use in the Unit 1 Experiment.

# Drawing Conclusions, pages 12–13

Hold up your book, point to the headings, and ask students, *What does this say?* Call on individual students to answer. Point to each picture and say, *Look at this picture. Look at the caption.* Read each caption aloud as students follow along in their books. Make sure students are looking at the correct picture and caption. Keep vocabulary explanations to a minimum for now.

## Teach Pages

Read the text aloud, or call on individual students to read it. Use pictures, drawings on the board, and mime to teach the meaning of new words. Help students with pronunciation.

Have students read the pages again to themselves. Alternatively, have pairs or small groups of students read aloud to each other.

**Understand Information** Ask comprehension and picture questions. Depending on students' abilities, you may want to ask more *yes-no* questions than *Wh-* questions. If helpful, write all or part of each question and answer on the board; alternatively, repeat the question and verbally model the type of response you expect.

Hold up your book as you ask questions such as, *What do scientists do after they observe? What is this called? What did the bean experiment test? Did the beans grow with water? Was the hypothesis correct? What is your conclusion? Can you think of more questions about the bean plant? What can you ask? What does a scientist continue to do?* Continue asking similar questions about all the pictures and the text.

**Organize Information** Draw a chart on the board with two columns. Ask, *What is step 5 of the scientific method?* Write the response in the chart. Say, *Let's add an example. What is an example of a conclusion?* Elicit a sentence and write it on the board. Have students add the information to the chart they started previously in their notebooks. The last part of the chart might look like this:

| Step 5: Drawing Conclusions | Example |
| --- | --- |
| After scientists observe, they decide if their hypothesis is correct. | The hypothesis is correct. Your conclusion is *seeds need water to grow.* |

Have students look at the scientific method flowchart on page 13. Have them copy this chart into their notebooks to help review and consolidate all five steps. Additionally, you may wish to have students write the steps on index cards and use them as flashcards.

**Before You Go On**

Do this exercise together as a class. Read or have a student read the first question, and have the class write it in their notebooks. Model the activity on the board. Ask students to look at the text. Have them find and read the sentence that answers the first question. Write the answer on the board and have students copy it into their notebooks. Complete the other questions in the same manner.

**Answers**

1. After scientists observe, they decide if their hypothesis is correct.
2. The conclusion is seeds need water to grow.
3. Possible answers: Will the bean plant continue to grow? Will it be a healthy plant? Does it need something else to grow well?

Workbook pages 5–6 may now be assigned for homework or done in class. Make sure that students understand how to complete the workbook pages by reading the directions with the class first. Go over the task on the page before students begin. Elicit the first few answers for each exercise.

## Safety, pages 14–15

### Preview Pages

Use the pictures to preview the pages. Encourage students to say whatever they can to describe them. Keep vocabulary explanations to a minimum for now.

### Teach Pages

Read the text aloud, or call on individual students to read it. Use pictures, drawings on the board, and mime to teach the meaning of new words. Help students with pronunciation.

Have students read the pages again to themselves. Alternatively, have pairs or small groups of students read aloud to each other.

**Understand Information** Ask comprehension and picture questions. Depending on students' abilities, you may want to ask more *yes-no* questions than *Wh-* questions. If helpful, write all or part of each question and answer on the board; alternatively, repeat the question and verbally model the type of response you expect.

Hold up your book as you ask questions such as, *What's very important in the science classroom? Who will the rules keep safe? What will you do to help you understand the scientific method? What will you learn first?* (pointing to the heading for the first safety rule) *What's this rule? What do you read carefully? What do you do before you begin? What do you do when you don't understand?* (pointing to the first picture) *What is this student doing?* (pointing to the next picture) *What's this girl using? What's this safety rule? Where do you point the scissors? Where do you point them when you carry them? Where do you keep your fingers?* Continue to ask similar questions about all the pictures and the text.

**Organize Information** Draw a chart on the board labeled *Safety Rules*. Point to the first heading and ask, *What is this rule?* Elicit the first couple of rules and write them in the chart. Then have students work individually or in pairs to complete their charts. After students are finished, elicit the information verbally. You may want to call on a student to read the text about each rule once more. The chart might look like this:

| Safety Rules | |
|---|---|
| **1.** Make sure you understand. | **5.** Clean up spills. |
| **2.** Be careful with scissors. | **6.** Be careful with electricity. |
| **3.** Stay away from broken glass. | **7.** Be careful with hot things. |
| **4**. Tell your teacher if you hurt yourself. | **8.** Keep things clean. |

## REACHING ALL STUDENTS: Kinesthetic Learners

Do a TPR exercise with the action verbs in the rules. Have student volunteers read aloud the text about each rule. Mime each motion as it is read. For example, for rule 1, act out reading, then raising your hand to ask a question. For rule 2, hold two fingers like scissors, point them away from your body, and mimic cutting; then point them down and move the fingers of your other hand far away from the "blades." For rule 3, "drop" a glass, then raise your hand. Go through a mime of the rules a second time with students, if helpful. Then invite student volunteers to mime each action while the rest of the class guesses the action and the rule.

### Before You Go On

Do this exercise together as a class. Read or have a student read the first question, and have the class write it in their notebooks. Ask students to look at the text. Have them find and read the sentence that answers that question. Write the answer on the board and have students copy it into their notebooks. Complete the other questions in the same manner.

**Answers**
1. We follow safety rules because they will keep us safe.
2. You need to be careful with scissors, broken glass, electricity, and hot things.
3. You carry scissors with the points down.

 Workbook pages 7–8 may now be assigned for homework or done in class. Make sure that students understand how to complete the workbook pages by reading the directions with the class first. Go over the task on the page before students begin. Elicit the first few answers for each exercise.

## Practicing the Scientific Method, pages 16–17
## Experiment, page 17

### Preview

With books closed, elicit and review the steps of the scientific method. Then say, *We're going to practice the scientific method. We're going to do an experiment.* Have students open their books. Point to and elicit the heading on page 16. Point to each picture and say, *Look at this picture. Look at the caption.* Read the captions on page 16 aloud as students follow along in their books. Ask questions about the captions, such as (pointing to the vase of flowers), *What are these? Where are these flowers? Why are they in water? What does* fresh *mean?* (pointing to the carnation) *What is this flower? What color are the petals? What color is the stem? How many leaves does it have?*

### Do the Experiment

For this experiment you will need two or more white carnations. Depending on your resources, have students do this experiment with a partner, in small groups, or as a class. Have students use the Experiment Log pages in their workbooks to make notes during the steps of the experiment.

Note that this is a two-day experiment; let the petals absorb the food coloring overnight before proceeding to the Draw Conclusions section.

Review with the class any relevant safety tips from pages 14–15. Make sure students know to be careful with glass and to clean up any spills right away.

Call on a student to read the experiment title. Say, *This is our main question.* Read aloud the purpose and materials, or have individual students read them. Read each of the What to Do instructions aloud. Ask comprehension questions.

After step 2, have students guess how the water goes up to the petals. Write their hypotheses on the board and have the class choose the most appropriate hypothesis for the experiment. Then have students perform each step.

Have students observe the flowers the next day. When they have done so, elicit conclusions from the class and write them on the board. Make sure that students complete both pages of the Experiment Log in their workbook.

Workbook pages 9–10 should be used to record the steps during the experiment and to draw pictures of what the flowers looked like before and after the experiment.

## Science Tools, pages 18–19

### Preview Pages

Use the pictures and captions to preview the pages. Encourage students to say whatever they can to describe the pictures. Keep vocabulary explanations to a minimum for now.

Read the text aloud, or call on individual students to read it. Use pictures, drawings on the board, and mime to teach the meaning of new words. Help students with pronunciation.

Have students read the pages again to themselves. Alternatively, have pairs or small groups of students read aloud to each other.

**Understand Information** Ask comprehension and picture questions. Depending on students' abilities, you may want to ask more *yes-no* questions than *Wh-*questions. If helpful, write all or part of each question and answer on the board; alternatively, repeat the question and verbally model the type of response you expect.

Hold up your book as you ask questions such as (pointing to the balance), *What is this? What does it measure?* (pointing to the thermometer) *What is this? What does it measure?* (pointing to the stopwatch) *What is this? What does it measure?* Continue asking similar questions about all the pictures and the text.

**Organize Information** Draw a chart on the board labeled *Science Tools* with two columns headed *Tool* and *Use*. Point to the balance and ask, *What is this? What's it used for?* Elicit the first couple of tools and uses to write in the chart. Then have students work individually or in pairs to complete the charts in their notebooks. Review the chart as a class. The chart might look like this:

| Science Tools | |
|---|---|
| **Tool** | **Use** |
| balance | measures how heavy something is |
| thermometer | measures how hot or cold something is |
| stopwatch | measures time |
| ruler | measures how long something is |
| hand lens | lets us see small things close up |
| camera | lets us take pictures |
| telescope | lets us see things far away in the sky |
| microscope | lets us see very small things |

## REACHING ALL STUDENTS: Kinesthetic Learners

Bring examples of some or all of these science tools to class. Set them up in different parts of the room. Show students how to use each tool. Then, in pairs or small groups, have students measure or observe something with each tool and record their findings in their notebooks. For example, have students measure a rock with the balance and record its weight. Have students measure a carnation and record its length in centimeters and inches. Have them look through a hand lens at a cross-section of a stem used in the experiment and then draw a picture.

**Before You Go On**

Do this exercise together as a class. Read or have a student read the first question, and have the class write it in their notebooks. Ask students to look at the text. Have them find and read the sentence that answers the question. Write the answer on the board and have students copy it into their notebooks. Complete the other questions in the same manner.

**Answers**

**1.** A thermometer measures how hot or cold something is.

**2.** A hand lens, a camera, a telescope, and a microscope have lenses.

**3.** A telescope lets us see things far away in the sky.

Workbook pages 11–12 may now be assigned for homework or done in class. Make sure that students understand how to complete the workbook pages by reading the directions with the class first. Go over the task on the page before students begin. Elicit the first few answers for each exercise.

## Visuals, pages 20–21

### Preview Pages

Point to the heading and ask students, *What does this say?* Point to each visual and say, *Look at this visual. Look at the caption.* Read each caption aloud as students follow along in their books. Make sure students are looking at the correct visual and caption. Keep vocabulary explanations to a minimum for now.

### Teach Pages

Read aloud the information at the top of the page, or call on individual students to read it. Have students reread silently. Ask, *What do scientists do after they learn information? What do they often use to share information?*

As this is just an introduction to the range of visuals students will encounter, keep the information to a minimum. The objective here is for students to be able to recognize the different visuals they will see in later units and to understand what they are used for.

**Understand Information**  Ask a few simple questions about each visual so that students can identify it, such as (pointing to the chart), *What visual is this? Is this visual a picture? What words do you know here? What numbers do you see?* (pointing to the diagram) *What visual is this? Is this visual a picture? What does this picture show? Which parts have names?* (pointing to the cycle diagram) *What's this? What do these pictures show? How are the arrows moving?* (pointing to the sectional diagram) *What's this? Is this visual a picture? What words do you know here?* Say, *A sectional diagram shows the inside of something.* (pointing to the pie chart) *What's this? What's a pie? What shape is this chart? What words and numbers can you see?* Continue asking similar questions about all the pictures and the text.

**Organize Information** Draw a chart on the board labeled *Visuals* with columns headed *Visual* and *Page*. Say, *Write the names of these visuals in your chart in your notebook.* Elicit the first couple of visuals and write them in the chart. Have students complete their charts as you complete the one on the board.

Say, *Let's find these visuals in the book. Then we'll write down the page number.* (pointing to the *chart* on the board) *Let's find a chart.* Model by flipping through your book, looking for a chart. Locate the chart on page 201, then hold up your book for the students to see. Say, *This is a chart. It's on page 201.* Write *201* into the chart. Then ask the class to find a picture of a diagram. Elicit a page number and write it on the board. Then have students work in small groups to look for examples and page numbers of all the visuals to complete their charts. Later, as a class, elicit the information and write it on the board. The chart might look like this:

| Visuals | | | |
|---|---|---|---|
| **Visual** | **Page** | **Visual** | **Page** |
| chart | 201, 207, 211 | pie chart | 79, 81, 89 |
| diagram | 31, 34, 39 | illustration | 30, 33, 35 |
| cycle diagram | 53, 55, 57 | photograph | 26, 27, 28 |
| sectional diagram | 99, 103, 109 | micrograph | 167, 175, 177 |

### Before You Go On

Do this exercise together as a class. Read or have a student read the first question, and have the class write it in their notebooks. Ask students to look at the text. Have them find and read the sentence that answers the question. Write the answer on the board and have students copy it into their notebooks. Complete the other questions in the same manner.

**Answers**
1. Scientists use visuals to share information.
2. Charts and pie charts give information using words and numbers.
3. Diagrams, cycle diagrams, sectional diagrams, illustrations, photographs, and micrographs use pictures.

 Workbook pages 13–14 may now be assigned for homework or done in class. Make sure that students understand how to complete the workbook pages by reading the directions with the class first. Go over the task on the page before students begin. Elicit the first few answers for each exercise.

# Science Reading Strategies, pages 22–23

## Preview Pages

Point to the headings and say, *This is a heading. What does this heading say?* Point to each picture and say, *Look at this picture. Look at the caption.* Read each caption aloud as students follow along in their books.

Write *Preview* on the board. Say, *We preview pages before we read. That's what we're doing now. We look at the headings, pictures, and captions. We also predict. We think about what will be next in the book.* Write *Strategies* on the board. Say, *Preview and predict are science reading strategies. Strategies can help us understand what we read.*

## Teach Pages

Read the text and the captions aloud, or call on individual students to read them. Use pictures, drawings on the board, and mime to teach the meaning of new words. Help students with pronunciation.

Have students read the pages again to themselves. Alternatively, have pairs or small groups of students read aloud to each other.

**Understand Information** Ask comprehension and picture questions. Depending on students' abilities, you may want to ask more *yes-no* questions than *Wh-* questions. If helpful, write all or part of each question and answer on the board; alternatively, repeat the question and verbally model the type of response you expect.

Hold up your book as you ask questions such as, *What will you use in this book? What are these strategies? What will these strategies do? What do you do when you preview? What do you look at? What are headings?* (pointing to the small preview page) *What are the headings in the small preview page? What else do you look at? What pictures do you see in the preview page? What are the words near them? What does* predict *mean? When do you predict? What do you predict?* (pointing to the picture of the girl) *What is this girl predicting?* Continue asking similar questions about all the pictures and the text.

Have students turn to pages 34–35. Say, *Let's preview and predict. What do you do when you preview? What are the headings? What do you see in the pictures and the words around them? What will you learn about?* Have students turn to pages 48–49. Say, *Preview and predict.* Give students a few moments to look at the pages. Then ask, *What will you learn about on these pages?*

**Organize Information** Make a two-column chart on the board. Label the columns *Preview* and *Predict.* Have students copy the chart into their notebooks. Ask students to reread the information and write an important idea about each reading strategy in the appropriate column. Check answers as a class by eliciting students' responses. Have students point to the places on the pages where they found their information.

**Before You Go On**

Do this exercise together as a class. Read or have a student read the first question, and have the class write it in their notebooks. Ask students to look at the text. Have them find and read the sentence that answers the question. Write the answer on the board and have students copy it into their notebooks. Complete the other questions in the same manner.

**Answers**

1. These strategies will help you understand and remember what you read.
2. You look at pages before you read them. You look at the headings. You also look at the pictures and the captions.
3. *Predict* means to guess what a text is about.

# Review and Practice, pages 24–25

## Check Your Understanding

Depending on the language level and abilities of your students, have them answer the questions individually, in pairs, or in small groups. If students need extra support, tell them to look at the information in their notebooks or allow students to look back at the text. Then have students share their answers with the class. Write the answers on the board.

**Answers**

1. c. Earth
2. b. Life
3. b. Physical
4. c. scientific method
5. a. hypothesis
6. b. observe
7. a. conclusions
8. b. tools
9. c. visuals
10. a. strategies

## Apply Science Skills

**Science Reading Strategy: Preview and Predict** Read the instructions aloud, or call on a student to read them. Review the science reading strategy by having students look at pages 22–23. Ask students, *How do you preview? What do you do when you predict? How does this help you?* Have students use the reduced version of the Student Book pages on page 25 or turn to pages 36–37. Work as a class to preview and predict.

Workbook pages 15–16 may now be assigned for homework or done in class. Make sure that students understand how to complete the workbook pages by reading the directions with the class first. Go over the task on the page before students begin. Elicit the first few answers for each exercise.

# Unit 1 Plants
## Unit Overview

| Lesson | Content | Science Skills | | Experiment |
| --- | --- | --- | --- | --- |
| | | **Reading Strategies** | **Using Visuals** | |
| 1 | • What Is a Plant?<br>• Parts of a Plant | Main Idea and Details | Diagrams | Do Plants Grow toward the Light? |
| 2 | • How Plants Work<br>• Photosynthesis<br>• Making New Plants<br>• The Plant Life Cycle | Compare and Contrast | Cycle Diagrams | |

## Objectives

**Vocabulary**
• Develop new vocabulary related to plants
• Use newly acquired vocabulary in context

**Concepts**
• Learn the parts of a plant and how they function
• Learn about photosynthesis
• Learn about the plant life cycle

**Reading Strategies**
• Recognize the main idea and details in a paragraph
• Use compare and contrast to understand what you read
• Practice previously learned strategies

**Using Visuals**
• Understand how to study diagrams for information
• Understand how to study cycle diagrams for information

**Experiment**
• Find out whether plants grow toward light

## Unit Opener, pages 26–27

**Preview Topic**

Hold up your book and point to the features on page 26. Ask students to preview the page. Remind students that when they preview a page, they look at the headings and pictures. Give students a few moments. Then ask, *What is this unit about?* Write the word *Predict* on the board and say, *Let's predict. What do you think you'll learn about plants?*

Ask students what they see in the pictures. Encourage them to say whatever they can. Write these words on the board. Point to each picture and give more information about it to reinforce the new vocabulary.

### Unit Concepts

Read aloud the list of unit concepts for Lesson 1. Draw simple pictures on the board to illustrate some of the concepts. For example, draw a plant with roots, stems, and leaves. Ask, *What words do you know here?* Tell students they'll learn the other words as they read the unit.

### Get Ready

Bring a potted or cut flower to show to the class, or use the carnations from the previous experiment. Point to the flower petals and ask, *What color is the flower? What shape is it?* Write the students' answers on the board. Say, *These are traits of the flower.* Write *Traits* on the board. Point to the leaves and ask, *What color are the leaves?* Write the students' answers on the board and say, *The color green is a trait of the leaves.*

Read the instructions and words on the chart aloud, or call on students to read them. Point to the chart and ask, *What four traits will you write about?* Teach *feel* and *smell*, if needed. Ask, *What two parts of a plant will you write about?* Tell students to copy the chart into their notebooks while you draw it on the board.

Since this is the first Get Ready activity, do it as a class. Ask students to come to the front in groups to look at, touch, and smell the flowers and leaves.

Call on volunteers to help you fill in the chart, prompting students with clues, if necessary. Complete the chart on the board as students answer, and have students complete it in their notebooks.

## Lesson 1

## Before You Read, pages 28–31

Hold up your book and ask students, *What do you look at when you preview? What are the headings? What do you see in the pictures? What will you learn on these pages?*

**Vocabulary**

Read the captions aloud, or call on students to read them. Help students understand and pronounce new words. Have students read the captions again silently or with a partner.

Ask picture and comprehension questions for each item. For example, point to the soil and ask, *What is this?* (pointing to the roots) *What are these? Are the roots growing deep in the soil? Do the roots take in water?* (pointing to the stem) *What is this? What does the stem do?* (pointing to the flowers) *How many petals does each flower have? What color are they? What do petals protect? What color are the inner parts of the flower?* (pointing to the seedling) *How many leaves does this plant have? What does the plant make in its leaves?* (pointing to the apple) *What is this? What's inside? What can seeds grow into?*

Point out the key words in the upper-right box on page 29. Read them aloud and have students say them after you. Say, *These words are important in this lesson. These words will help you understand the lesson.*

Have students close their books. Hold up your book so that all students can see. Point to pictures illustrating the key words at random. For each picture, ask the class, *What is this?* or *What are these?* Encourage students to respond chorally.

## Practice

Have students write the sentences in their notebooks, leaving a space for the answer. Model by writing the first sentence on the board. When most students have finished writing, model choosing an answer and filling in the blank for sentence 1. Model thinking aloud by asking the class, *Do seeds protect the inner parts of the flower? Do petals protect the inner parts of the flower?* (yes) *Do leaves protect the inner part of the flower?* (no) *So the answer is petals.* Individually or in pairs, have students choose the correct answers and write them in the sentences. Check answers by calling on individual students to read their sentences aloud. Write the letters of the correct answers on the board.

---

**Answers**

**1.** b. petals     **3.** a. roots     **5.** b. Seeds
**2.** b. leaves     **4.** c. soil      **6.** c. stem

---

Workbook page 17 may now be assigned for homework or done in class. This page provides practice in understanding and using the key words.

## Science Skills

**Science Reading Strategy: Main Idea and Details** With books closed, write the following paragraph on the board and have a student read it aloud:

> An apple is a fruit. It
> is sweet. It has seeds.
> It is red or green.

Draw a box and write *Main Idea* inside. Ask students, *What is the main sentence in this paragraph? What is the most important idea?* Write the correct response in the box. Draw a line from this box to a new box below and write *Detail* inside. Tell students, *The other sentences in this paragraph are details. They give us more information about the main idea.* Ask, *What are some details about an apple?*

Write the correct responses in the chart. The chart might look like this:

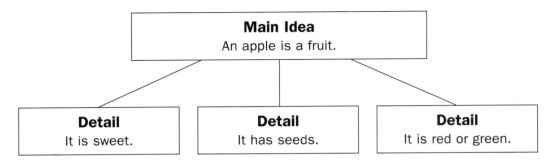

**Main Idea**
An apple is a fruit.

**Detail**
It is sweet.

**Detail**
It has seeds.

**Detail**
It is red or green.

Have students open their books to page 30. Ask them to cover the chart with their notebook. Model with your own book. Read the introduction or call on students to read it aloud. Have students reread it again silently, if helpful. Explain any new words.

Read or call on individual students to read the passage aloud. Teach any new words. Draw a box on the board. Label it *Main Idea*. Tell students to reread the paragraph silently and look for the main idea. When they are finished, elicit the main idea and write it in the box. Point out that the main idea is often the first sentence in a paragraph. Then draw a *Detail* box. Elicit details in order, but don't write them on the board. Have students uncover the chart on page 30. Ask students to copy the chart into their notebooks. Tell them to add one more detail from the passage to the chart. Model by drawing three more *Detail* boxes on the board. When students have finished, elicit the fourth detail. (The smell attracts flies and other insects.) Write it on the board. Remind students to look for the main idea and details as they read.

Workbook page 18 may now be assigned for homework or done in class. Make sure that students understand how to complete the workbook page by reading the directions with the class first. Go over the task on the page before students begin.

**Using Visuals: Diagrams** Hold up your book and remind students that scientists often use visuals to share information. Point to the diagram of the flowering plant and ask, *What does this diagram show?*

Read aloud the information on the page, or call on individual students to read it. Help students understand and pronounce any new words. Have students reread silently, if helpful. Ask students, *What is a diagram? Can you point to a label? What do these diagrams show? What does the plant on the left have? Do ferns have flowers?* Point to each diagram and ask, *What does this diagram show?* Point to each label, say the word, and have students repeat after you. Have students study the diagrams for a minute. Then read question 1 aloud. Elicit the answer and write it on the board. Have students copy the question and answer into their notebooks. Do the same for the other two questions.

**Answers**
1. The leaf of a fern is called a frond.
2. The stem of the fern is in the soil.
3. Possible answers: Their roots are in the soil. Their leaves are green.

Workbook pages 19–20 may now be assigned for homework or done in class. Make sure that students understand how to complete the workbook pages by reading the directions with the class first. Go over the tasks on the pages before students begin.

## Lesson ❶

## What Is a Plant? pages 32–33

### Preview Pages

Hold up your book, point to the heading, and ask students, *What does this say?* Call on individual students to answer. Point to each picture and say, *Look at this picture. Look at the caption.* Read each caption aloud as students follow along in their books. Make sure students are looking at the correct picture and caption. Keep vocabulary explanations to a minimum for now, but encourage students to say whatever they can about the pages.

### Teach Pages

Write the key words (page 29) on the board before students begin. Read the text aloud, or call on individual students to read it. Use pictures, drawings on the board, and mime to teach the meaning of new words. Help students with pronunciation.

Ask if students found any key words. (leaves, roots) Have volunteers read the sentences containing the key words.

Have students read the pages again to themselves. Alternatively, have students read aloud to each other in pairs or small groups.

**Understand Information** Ask comprehension and picture questions. Depending on students' abilities, you may want to ask more *yes-no* questions than *Wh-* questions. If helpful, write all or part of each question and answer on the board; alternatively, repeat the question and model an appropriate verbal response.

Hold up your book as you ask questions such as, *What do we know about plants? Are some good to eat? What plants are good to eat?* (This is a thinking question; elicit several examples.) *Are plants living things? What are they part of? Are plants the same as animals in some ways? How? What do plants need? Do animals need food and water, too? Do plants make new plants? What's another way to say "make new plants"? What happens to plants in time? Do animals die, too? Are plants different from animals in important ways? What do animals have to do? What do animals eat? Where do plants make food? What is another difference? Do plants move from place to place by themselves? What keeps plants in the ground?* Continue asking similar questions about all the pictures and the text.

**Organize Information** Draw a blank Main Idea and Details chart on the board. Have students look at the first paragraph on page 32. Ask them to find the main idea. Tell them that in this paragraph it's a question. Elicit the answer and write it in your chart.

Have students copy the chart into their notebooks and complete it. Then check answers and complete the chart on the board. The chart might look like this:

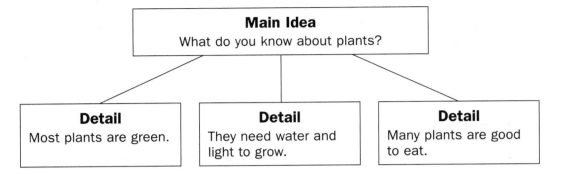

```
┌─────────────────────────────────────┐
│              Main Idea               │
│      What do you know about plants?  │
└─────────────────────────────────────┘
```

| Detail | Detail | Detail |
|--------|--------|--------|
| Most plants are green. | They need water and light to grow. | Many plants are good to eat. |

**Language Tip:** Plural Nouns

Have students look at the Language Tip box on page 32. Read the text aloud, or call on a student to read it. Write these words on the board: *flower, petal, seed, root, stem.* Ask, *How do we make the plural for* flower? (add *-s*) Write the plural *flowers* next to *flower* on the board and have students write the two words in their notebooks. Do the same for the other words. Assist students with the pronunciation of plurals, pointing out the two different sounds /s/ and /z/ for the letter *s*.

**As You Read:** Main Idea and Details

Point to the As You Read box on page 33. Read the text aloud, or call on a student to read it. Point to the first paragraph on page 33. Have students read this paragraph again and find the main idea and details. Give students a few minutes to reread the paragraph. Then elicit the main idea (Plants are different from animals in important ways.) and details (Most plants do not need to eat. Plants make food in their leaves. Animals have to eat to stay alive. Animals eat plants or other animals.). Write the details in a chart on the board.

## Optional Activity

Teach the names of plants we eat. Gather 8 to 12 pictures of common plant foods from the Internet or other resources. (carrots, broccoli, lettuce, cabbage, peas, corn, tomatoes, apples, bananas, oranges, pears, and so on) Show pictures of each item and elicit or teach the name as you write it on the board. Have students copy the names into their notebooks. Go through the pictures again in order, erasing the names on the board. Then scramble the pictures and elicit the names in random order.

Have pairs of students read the first two questions and find the sentences in the text that answer them. Have students write the questions and answers in their notebooks. Check answers before going on.

   Answer the third question together as a class. Tell students that this is a thinking question. Discuss possible answers and write them on the board. Have students copy them into their notebooks.

**Answers**

1. Plants and animals need food and water. They both reproduce. They grow old and, in time, die.
2. Most plants do not need to eat. Plants make food in their leaves. Plants do not move from place to place by themselves. Plants have roots.
3. Possible answers: They move up and out as they grow. The air/wind moves plants. They grow toward the light. People and animals move plants.

## Parts of a Plant, page 34
### Roots, page 35

### Preview Pages

Hold up your book, point to the headings, and ask students, *What does this say?* Call on individual students to answer. Point to each picture and say, *Look at this picture. Look at the caption.* Read each caption aloud as students follow along in their books. Make sure students are looking at the correct picture and caption. Keep vocabulary explanations to a minimum for now, but encourage students to say whatever they can about the pages.

### Teach Pages

Have the key words (page 29) on the board before students begin. Read the text or call on individual students to read it aloud. Use pictures, drawings on the board, and mime to teach the meaning of new words. Help students with pronunciation.

   Ask if students found any key words. (roots, stem, leaves, soil) Ask for a volunteer to read sentences containing the key words. Point to pictures of the key words on the page and ask, *What's this?* or *What are these?*

   Have students read the pages again to themselves. Alternatively, have students read aloud to each other in pairs or small groups.

**Understand Information** Ask comprehension and picture questions such as, *Do all plants look the same? What parts do most plants have? Why do the parts work together? What parts are usually above the ground? What parts are usually under the ground? What keeps a plant in the ground? What do roots take from the soil? What else do some roots do? What kind of root do some plants have? Is this kind of root easy to pull out of the ground? What's another kind of root? Are plants with many roots hard to pull out of the ground? What does the diagram show?* Continue asking similar questions about both pictures and the text.

**Organize Information** As a class activity, have students make a T-chart about different types of roots. Draw a T-chart on the board with the heading *Roots*. Point out that this kind of chart is called a T-chart. Have students copy the chart into their notebooks. Ask, *What are two types of roots?* Encourage students to look at page 35, if helpful. Write their answers in the chart. Ask, *What are two details about one main root?* and then, *What is one detail about a plant with many roots?* Fill in the chart with student answers and have students copy the chart into their notebooks. The chart might look like this:

| Roots | |
|---|---|
| **One main root** | **Many smaller roots** |
| Grows deep in the soil | Come out of the ground more easily |
| Hard to pull out | |

---

**Language Tip:** Spelling Change: *-f* or *-fe* to *-ves*

Read the text in the Language Tip box aloud. Write the words *leaf* and *leaves* on the board, model the pronunciation, and have students repeat. Have students find each word on page 34. Ask, *Which is the singular form? Which is the plural form?* Write *-f* or *-fe* ⟶ *-ves* on the board. Tell students, *Words ending in* -f *or* -fe *often change to* -ves *for the plural.* Elicit or give several other examples of words ending in *-f* or *-fe* and write them on the board under *leaf.* (life, self, shelf, half) Ask students to copy the words into their notebooks and write the plural form next to each one. Check answers as a class.

---

**Before You Go On**

Have pairs of students read the first two questions and find the sentences in the text that answer them. Have them write the questions and answers in their notebooks. Check answers before going on.

Answer the third question together as a class. Tell students that this is a thinking question. Simplify the question, if helpful. Say, *You pull a plant out of the ground. It dies. Why does it die?* Elicit answers from students and write them on the board. Have students copy them into their notebooks.

**Answers**
1. Most plants have roots, a stem, leaves, and flowers.
2. They keep plants in the ground. Roots take in water and nutrients from the soil. Some roots also store food for the plant.
3. Possible answers: The roots can't take in water or nutrients from the soil. The roots dry up.

## Preview Pages

Hold up your book, point to the headings, and ask students, *What does this say?* Call on individual students to answer. Point to each picture and say, *Look at this picture. Look at the caption.* Read each caption aloud as students follow along in their books. Make sure students are looking at the correct picture and caption. Keep vocabulary explanations to a minimum for now, but encourage students to say whatever they can about the pages.

## Teach Pages

Have the key words (page 29) on the board before students begin. Read the text aloud or call on individual students to read it. Elicit or explain the meanings of new words, and help students pronounce them.

Ask if students found any key words. (stem, leaves, roots) Ask for volunteers to read the sentences containing these words.

Have students read the pages again to themselves. Alternatively, have students read aloud to each other in pairs or small groups.

**Understand Information** Ask comprehension and picture questions such as, *What does a stem hold up? Why does it hold up the plant's leaves? What else does the stem do? Where does water enter the plant? Where does the stem carry the water? What does the diagram show? How do the leaves use the water? What else does the stem carry? What are the two main types of leaves?* Continue asking similar questions about all the pictures and the text.

**Organize Information** Draw a blank Main Idea and Details chart on the board. Have students look at the first paragraph on page 36. Ask them to find the main idea. If helpful, remind them that the main idea is often the first sentence. Elicit the answer and write it on the board. Have students work with a classmate to find the details that support the main idea. Check answers as a class. The chart might look like this:

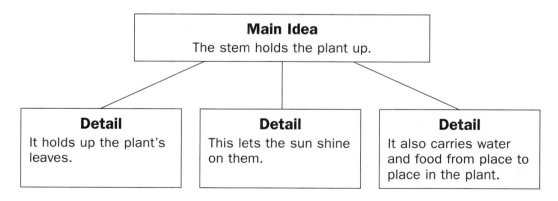

## REACHING ALL STUDENTS: Visual Learners

This exercise will help students better understand the functions of a leaf. Tell students that they will make a diagram of the information in the last paragraph on page 37. Ask students to reread that paragraph. Then draw a leaf on the board and have students copy it into their notebooks. Ask students, *How does a leaf take in and give off gases?* (through tiny holes in the bottom of the leaves) Ask students to draw these tiny holes on the leaf. Model the drawing on the board. Write *gases* near the picture of the leaf. Ask, *How can we show that the leaf takes in and gives off gases?* Draw lines with arrows pointing up and down from the leaf to *gases*. Ask, *What else does the leaf let out?* (water vapor) Call on a student to show the answer on the board. Have students complete the labels in their diagrams.

## Science at Home: Annual Rings

Have students look at the title and the photograph to predict what the text might be about. Read the text aloud, or call on a student to read it. Elicit or explain the meanings of new words, and help students pronounce them. Draw a diagram on the board to illustrate the text. Have students copy the diagram into their notebooks. The diagram might look like this:

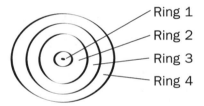

This tree is 4 years old.

Have students count the rings of the tree trunk pictured on page 36. Have them count the rings in pairs and write down approximately how old the tree is. Remind students that one ring has both light and dark wood. Elicit answers from several pairs. (The tree is 20 years old.)

## Language Tip: Homophones

Read the text in the Language Tip box aloud. Write the words *two* and *too* on the board. Have students find each word on page 37 and read them aloud. Ask, *Do you know another word that sounds like* two *and* too? (the preposition *to*) *How do you spell it? Use it in a sentence.* Teach other homophones (words that sound alike but have different spellings and meanings) by writing one word on the board and then eliciting a homophone and a sentence using it. Examples of basic homophones are: *four/for, there/they're/their, right/write, you're/your, know/no, buy/by/bye.* Have students copy these words into their notebooks.

In pairs, have students read the first two questions and find the sentences in the text that answer them. Have them write the questions and answers in their notebooks. Check answers before going on.

Do the third question together as a class. This question requires critical thinking. Encourage discussion before writing student answers on the board. Then have students copy the answers into their notebooks.

**Answers**

1. The stem holds the plant up. It holds the plant's leaves up. The stem also carries water and food from place to place in the plant.
2. There are two main types of leaves: broad leaves and needles.
3. The plant makes food in the leaves. As a plant makes food, it takes in and gives off gases. Sometimes a plant has too much water in it. Then the leaves let out water vapor through tiny holes.

# Exploring, page 38

## Preview Page

Hold up your book, point to the heading, and ask students, *What does this say?* Call on individual students to answer. Have students notice that the design of this page is different from other reading pages. Tell them that each unit has an Exploring page. Point to each picture and say, *Look at this picture. What is it?* Read each caption aloud as students follow along in their books. Make sure students are looking at the correct picture and caption. Keep vocabulary explanations to a minimum for now, but encourage students to say whatever they can about the pages.

## Teach Page

Read the text aloud, or call on individual students to read it. Elicit or explain the meanings of new words, using pictures in the text or on the board; help students pronounce them.

Have students read the page again to themselves. Alternatively, have students read aloud to each other in pairs or small groups.

**Understand Information** Ask comprehension and picture questions such as, *In what types of places do plants live?* (pointing to the picture of water lilies) *What plant is this? Where do water lilies live? Where are their stems? Where do their roots grow?* (pointing to the picture of a cactus) *What plant is this? Where does it live? What are cactus leaves called? What do they look like? How do they help the cactus? Why?*

Ask critical-thinking questions such as, *What holds up the water lilies' leaves?* (the water) *Can you see the cactus's stem?* (yes, it's the green part) *Where does the cactus hold water?* (in the stem)

**Organize Information** Say, *Let's make a Main Idea and Details chart about water lilies.* Draw a blank chart on the board and ask, *What is the main idea in the paragraph about water lilies?* (Water lilies live in water.) *What are the details?*

(They have broad leaves that float. They have long stems under the water. Their roots grow in the mud.) Have students complete a Main Idea and Details chart in their notebooks. Then ask volunteers to complete the chart on the board.

## Flowers, page 39

### Preview Page

Hold up your book, point to the heading, and ask students, *What does this say?* Call on individual students to answer. Point to the flower and say, *Look at this picture. Look at the caption.* Read the caption and the labels around the flower as students follow along in their books. Keep vocabulary explanations to a minimum for now, but encourage students to say whatever they can about the pages.

### Teach Page

Have the key words (page 29) on the board before students begin. Read the text aloud, or call on individual students to read it. Elicit or explain the meanings of new words, and help students pronounce them.

Ask if students found any key words. (seeds, petals) Have volunteers read the sentences containing these words. Ask students if they see any pictures of petals.

Have students read the page again to themselves. Alternatively, have students read aloud to each other in pairs or small groups.

**Understand Information** Ask comprehension and picture questions such as, *Do most plants have flowers? What do flowers help the plant do? What's the flower's main job? Where are the seeds? What do seeds grow into? What do the petals protect? What two kinds of parts does a flower have? Which part of a flower becomes the fruit? What do the labels on the diagram show?*

**Organize Information** Draw a blank Main Idea and Details chart on the board. Have students look at the first paragraph on page 39. Ask them to find the main idea. Tell them that in this paragraph the first sentence is not the main idea. Elicit the answer and write it on the board. Have students work in pairs to find the details that support the main idea. Check answers as a class. The chart might look like this:

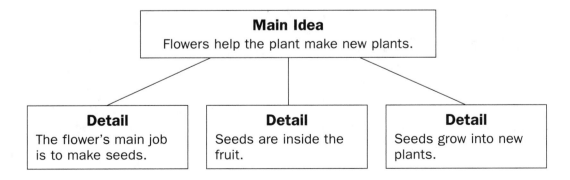

**Main Idea**
Flowers help the plant make new plants.

**Detail**
The flower's main job is to make seeds.

**Detail**
Seeds are inside the fruit.

**Detail**
Seeds grow into new plants.

**ART CONNECTION:** Vincent van Gogh

Read the paragraph aloud or call on individual students to read it. Elicit or explain the meanings of new words, using pictures in the text or on the board. Help students pronounce the words. Have students read the paragraph again to themselves.

Ask a few comprehension and picture questions such as, *What do they call a person who paints pictures? Did artists paint pictures of flowers many years ago?* (pointing to the picture) *Who painted this picture? When did he paint it? What kind of flowers are these? What other kinds of flowers did he paint?* Bring in a book, reproductions, or downloaded photos, or find websites showing flower paintings by van Gogh and others. Have students look at the pictures and say whatever they can. Encourage students to talk about which paintings they like.

## Before You Go On

In pairs, have students read the first two questions and find the sentences in the text that answer them. Have them write the questions and answers in their notebooks. Check answers before going on.

Answer the third question together as a class. This question requires critical thinking. Encourage discussion before writing student answers on the board. Have students copy the answers into their notebooks.

### Answers
1. The flower's main job is to make seeds.
2. The petals protect the parts inside the flower.
3. Possible answers: The main job of the fruit is to protect the seeds inside the fruit or provide a method for seeds to be carried.

 For more information, go to www.longmanusa.com/science for links to interesting websites about plants.

# Review and Practice, pages 40–41

## Vocabulary

If students need help in reviewing the vocabulary, see the Optional Vocabulary Activities (pages vii–viii) and choose an appropriate activity.

Suggest to students that they copy all the sentences into their notebooks before they begin writing the answers. Have students complete this exercise individually. Check answers as a class.

### Answers
1. leaves
2. roots
3. petals
4. soil
5. stem
6. seeds

## Check Your Understanding

Depending on the language level and abilities of the students, have them answer the questions individually, in pairs, or in small groups. If students need extra support, tell them to look at the information in their notebooks or allow students to look back at the text. Then have students share their answers with the class. Write the answers on the board.

---

**Answers**
1. The roots, stem, leaves, and flower are four parts of a plant.
2. The stem holds the plant/the leaves up. The stem also carries water and food from place to place in the plant.
3. The leaves make food for the plant. As a plant makes food, leaves take in and give off gases.
4. The female part of a flower becomes the fruit.

---

## Apply Science Skills

**Science Reading Strategy: Main Idea and Details**  Review the science reading strategy. Ask students, *What is the main idea in a paragraph? What are the details?*

Read the instructions aloud. Have students copy the chart into their notebooks and work in pairs to complete it. Circulate and offer assistance, if needed. Check answers by calling on students to complete the chart on the board. The completed chart might look like this:

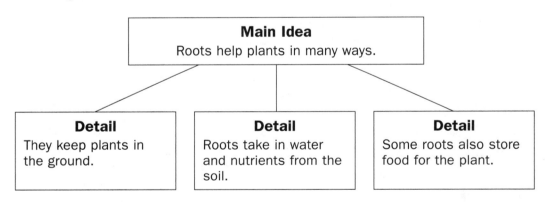

**Main Idea**
Roots help plants in many ways.

**Detail**
They keep plants in the ground.

**Detail**
Roots take in water and nutrients from the soil.

**Detail**
Some roots also store food for the plant.

**Using Visuals: Diagrams**  Read the heading and the instructions aloud, or call on individual students to read them. Help students understand and pronounce new words. Have students reread silently, if helpful.

Allow a few minutes for students to study the diagram. Then have pairs of students ask and answer the first two questions. Have them write their answers in their notebooks.

Do the third question together as a class. Elicit as many answers to question 3 as possible. Write the answers on the board.

> **Answers**
> 1. They both have petals, pollen, a female part, and male parts. They both have stems.
> 2. The flower is open. You can see pink and white petals. The bud is not open, and the parts are all together.
> 3. Possible answers: You can see which way the bud is pointing. The bud is pointing up toward the sun. You can see the stem.

## Discuss

Read the discussion questions aloud. Have students discuss the questions as a class. Encourage them to offer reasons or examples for their opinions.

 Workbook pages 21–22 may now be assigned for homework or done in class. These pages provide extra practice in the same categories as the Review and Practice pages in the Student Book.

## Evaluation

### Self-Assessment Questions

Write the following questions on the board and have students respond in their notebooks. Encourage students to share their responses in small groups or as a class.
1. How can I use the main idea and details to help me in reading?
2. How can diagrams help me understand new ideas?
3. What was difficult for me in this lesson?
4. What was easy for me in this lesson?
5. What was most enjoyable in this lesson?

# Lesson ②

# Before You Read, pages 42–45

Have students look back at the unit opener on pages 26 and 27. Have students look at the list of concepts for Lesson 2. Read them aloud. Ask, *What words do you know here?* Write any words students know on the board. Ask students what the words mean. Tell students they'll learn the other words as they read the lesson.

   Ask students to preview the title, pictures, and captions on pages 42–43. Then ask, *What do you think you will learn?*

## Vocabulary

Read the captions aloud, or call on individual students to read them. Help students understand and pronounce new words. Have students read the captions again silently.

   Ask picture and comprehension questions for each item, such as, *What are heat and light? Where does most energy come from? How do plants use the energy in light? What is this process called? What do the male parts of a flower make? What color is pollen? Can you point to the pollen in the picture?* (pointing to the picture of a seed)

*What is this seed doing? What is this process called?* (pointing to the picture of a butterfly) *What insect is this? How do insects help flowers? What is this process called?*

Point out the key words in the upper-right box on page 43. Read them aloud and have students say them after you. Say, *These words are important in this lesson. These words will help you understand the lesson.*

## Practice

Read the instructions and the example aloud. Have students copy the example definition into their notebooks. In pairs or small groups, have students define the other words. Check answers by calling on individual students to read their sentences aloud. Write their definitions on the board, correcting as necessary.

> **Possible Answers**
> • energy: heat and light; almost all comes from the sun
> • germination: the process of a seed beginning to grow roots
> • insects: they carry pollen from flower to flower; a butterfly is an insect
> • photosynthesis: the process of plants using energy in light to make food
> • pollen: the male parts of a flower make pollen; it is often yellow

Workbook page 23 may now be assigned for homework or done in class. This workbook page provides practice in understanding and using the key words.

## Science Skills

**Science Reading Strategy: Compare and Contrast** Write *Compare and Contrast* on the board. Tell students, *When we compare, we say how things are the same. When we contrast, we say how things are different.* Hold up a pen and a pencil. Draw a Venn diagram on the board. Say, *Let's compare and contrast.* Ask the class, *How is a pen different from a pencil? How are they the same?* Write the responses on the board in the Venn diagram. Prompt students with ideas if they get stuck.

Read aloud the information and instructions at the top of page 44, or call on individual students to read them. Help students pronounce any new words. Have students reread silently, if helpful.

Call on individual students to read the information in the Venn diagram aloud. Remind students that the circle labeled *Orange* shows how it is different from the banana, and the middle circle shows how the fruits are the same.

Tell students that the class is going to choose two different fruits to compare and contrast. Help students decide on the fruits. Then write them in a diagram on the board and ask students to copy the diagram into their notebooks. Ask, *How is (Fruit 1) different from (Fruit 2)? How is (Fruit 2) different from (Fruit 1)? How are they the same?* Write the responses on the board in the Venn diagram and have students copy it. Alternatively, have students compare and contrast two fruits of their choice individually or in pairs.

Workbook pages 24–25 may now be assigned for homework or done in class. Make sure students understand how to complete the workbook page by reading the directions with the class first. Then go over the task on the page before students begin.

**Using Visuals: Cycle Diagrams** Have students read the heading on the top of page 45. Ask students, *What visual did you learn about in Lesson 1?* (diagrams) If necessary, have them look back in their books. Ask, *What visual will you practice using in this lesson?*

Read aloud or call on individual students to read the information at the top of page 45 and the labels on the cycle diagram. Help students understand and pronounce the new words. Have students reread silently, if helpful.

Allow students a few minutes to study the diagram. Then, depending on the level of the students, have students ask and answer the questions in pairs or as a class. Have students write their answers in their notebooks.

---

**Answers**
1. The fruit forms.
2. The fruit falls.
3. Because it shows that things happen again and again in the same order.

---

Workbook page 26 may now be assigned for homework or done in class. Make sure that students understand how to complete the workbook page by reading the directions with the class first. Then go over the task on the page before students begin.

## Lesson ❷

# How Plants Work, pages 46–53
## Photosynthesis, pages 46–47

### Preview Pages

Hold up your book, point to the headings, and ask students, *What does this say?* Call on individual students to answer. Point to each picture and say, *Look at this picture. Look at the caption.* Read each caption aloud as students follow along in their books. Make sure students are looking at the correct picture and caption. Keep vocabulary explanations to a minimum for now, but encourage students to say whatever they can about the pages.

### Teach Pages

Have the key words (page 43) on the board before students begin. Read the text aloud or call on individual students to read it. Elicit or explain the meanings of new words, and help students pronounce them.

Ask if students found any key words. (photosynthesis, energy) Have volunteers read sentences containing the key words.

Have students read the pages again to themselves. Alternatively, have students read aloud to each other in pairs or small groups.

**Understand Information** Ask comprehension questions such as, *How do plants make food? What does* photo *mean in Greek? What does* synthesis *mean? So what does* photosynthesis *mean? What do plants use to make food? Where does the light usually come from? Where do plants get energy? Can you see sunlight in the photograph and diagram? How do plants use the energy from sunlight?* (pointing to the glossed words) *What is carbon dioxide? What is oxygen? What is the plant's food? What goes out into the air? Who needs oxygen to breathe?*

Have students focus on the diagram. Point to the labels, if needed. Ask, *What does this diagram show? What is the leaf taking in? What is made inside the leaf? What does the leaf give off?* (pointing to the equation near the bottom of the diagram) *What does water and carbon dioxide become?* Continue asking similar questions about all the pictures and the text.

**Organize Information** As a class, make a sequence diagram showing photosynthesis and how it helps people and animals. Draw five boxes on the board with arrows connecting them. Write *Sequence Diagram* on the board. Say, *This is a sequence diagram.* (pointing to each box) *It shows what happens first, next, and after that. Let's do a sequence diagram about photosynthesis.* Write *Photosynthesis* above the diagram. Ask, *Where does a plant get energy to make oxygen?* Write the answer in the first box. Ask, *How does a plant's oxygen help people and other animals?* Write the answer in the last box. Then have students complete the diagram in pairs or groups. Check by eliciting information and writing it on the board. The diagram might look like this:

## Photosynthesis

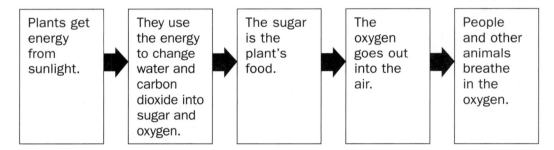

| Plants get energy from sunlight. | → | They use the energy to change water and carbon dioxide into sugar and oxygen. | → | The sugar is the plant's food. | → | The oxygen goes out into the air. | → | People and other animals breathe in the oxygen. |

---

### Environment Watch: Rain Forests

Have students look at the photograph of a rain forest on page 46. Ask, *What do you see in this photo? What are the leaves doing with the energy from the sun? Who needs oxygen to breathe? Do you think many animals live in this forest? Do you think many insects live there?* Have students look at the picture of the rain forest after the trees have been cut down. Ask, *What do you see in this photo? Can the cut trees make oxygen? Can many animals and insects live here now?* Ask students to compare and contrast what they see in the two photos.

Read the text aloud, or call on individual students to read it. Help students pronounce the words. Have students read the passage again to themselves. Ask comprehension questions about the passage.

## Optional Activity

Conduct further research on the Internet to find rain forest pictures. Help students learn new vocabulary through the pictures. Find rain forest locations on a world map.

---

**Language Tip:** Compound Words

Read the text in the Language Tip box aloud. Write *sun + light = sunlight* on the board. Ask for the definition of each word. Say, *Some words, like sunlight, are made of two words combined, or put together, to make a new word. This is called a compound word.* Give other examples such as, *note + book = notebook, back + pack = backpack.* Ask students for examples. Tell students to look for compound words as they read.

---

**HISTORY CONNECTION:** Discovering Oxygen

Read the text, or call on individual students to read it aloud. Elicit or explain the meanings of new words, using pictures in the text or on the board; help students pronounce the words. Have students read the passage again to themselves.

Ask comprehension and picture questions such as, W*hat did Joseph Priestley discover? When did he discover it? What did he do first? What happened to the candle? What did he do then? What happened this time? What did Priestly guess? What gas helped the candle burn? Can a candle burn without oxygen?*

---

**Before You Go On**

In pairs, have students read the first two questions and find the sentences in the text that answer them. Have them write the questions and answers in their notebooks. Check answers before going on.

Answer the third question together as a class. This question requires critical thinking. Encourage discussion before writing student answers on the board. Have students copy the answers into their notebooks.

### Answers
1. Photosynthesis is a process. Plants use light to make food.
2. Water and carbon dioxide change into sugar and oxygen during photosynthesis.
3. Possible answers: Plants make oxygen. People and other animals need oxygen to breathe. We need plants for food.

---

## Making New Plants, pages 48–49

### Preview Pages

Hold up your book, point to the heading, and ask students, *What does this say?* Call on individual students to answer. Point to each picture and say, *Look at this picture. Look at the caption.* Read each caption aloud as students follow along in their books. Make sure students are looking at the correct picture and caption.

**Teach Pages**

Have the key words (page 43) on the board before students begin. Read the text aloud or call on individual students to read it. Elicit or explain the meanings of new words, and help students pronounce them. Ask if students found any key words. (pollen, pollination, insects) Ask for volunteers to read sentences containing these words.

**Understand Information** Ask comprehension and picture questions such as, *What kind of plants are most plants? What does this mean? What do most seed plants produce? What does* produce *mean? What's inside the fruit? What protects the seeds? Do all seed plants produce fruit? What's an example of a seed plant that doesn't produce fruit? Where are the seeds of a pine tree? What do most seed plants have?* Continue asking similar questions about all the pictures and the text.

**Organize Information** Have students do a sequence diagram of how a bee might pollinate a flower. Write *Pollination* on the board. Ask students, *How does a bee pollinate a flower? What happens next?* Draw a blank sequence diagram on the board. Have students complete the diagram in pairs or groups. Check answers by eliciting information and writing it on the board. The diagram might look like this:

## Pollination

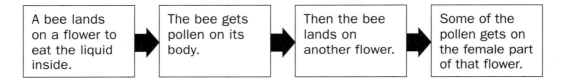

| A bee lands on a flower to eat the liquid inside. | → | The bee gets pollen on its body. | → | Then the bee lands on another flower. | → | Some of the pollen gets on the female part of that flower. |

**As You Read:** Compare and Contrast

Point to the As You Read section on page 48. Read it aloud, or call on a student to read it. Have students read page 48 again and think about the question. Then elicit how the pine tree is the same as and different from other seed plants. Make a Venn diagram on the board, telling students that this type of diagram is excellent for comparing and contrasting. The diagram might look like this:

**Pine Trees**
• don't produce fruit
• seeds are in cones
• cones protect the seeds

**Both**
• have seeds
• use seeds to make new plants
• are seed plants

**Other Seed Plants**
• produce fruit
• seeds are inside the fruit
• fruit protects the seeds

## Language Tip: Word Families

Read the text in the Language Tip box aloud, or have a volunteer read it to the class. Write these words on the board for students to copy: *pollen, pollinate, pollination.* Point out the pollen in the picture on page 49, and write on the board, *Pollen is usually yellow.* Ask, *Is* pollen *a noun or a verb in this sentence?* (a noun) Write *noun* next to *pollen* on the board. Point to the picture of the bee and say, *This bee pollinates other flowers.* Write this on the board and ask, *Is* pollinate *a noun or a verb?* (a verb) Say and write on the board, *The way a female part gets pollen is called pollination. Is* pollination *a noun or a verb?* (a noun) Point out that words ending in *-tion* are nouns, and underline this part of the word. Read the words aloud and have students repeat. Ask, *Do the first two syllables sound the same in each word?* (yes) *How does the spelling change?* (The *e* changes to an *i* in *pollinate* and *pollination.*)

Give students another example using *germ, germinate,* and *germination.*

## REACHING ALL STUDENTS: Auditory and Kinesthetic Learners

Read a list of characteristics of a papaya and a pinecone. Have students listen carefully to each characteristic. Have them raise one finger if it is a characteristic of one of the plants, and two fingers if it is a shared characteristic of both a papaya and a pinecone.

### Before You Go On

In pairs, have students read the first two questions and find the sentences in the text that answer them. Have them write the questions and answers in their notebooks. Check answers before going on.

Answer the third question together as a class. Elicit or teach the word *wind*, if needed. Tell students that this is a thinking question. Discuss possible answers. Write the answers on the board and have students copy them into their notebooks.

#### Answers
1. Seed plants use seeds to make new plants.
2. Insects carry pollen from flower to flower.
3. The wind moves/blows the pollen into the air. The pollen lands on another flower.

## Making New Plants (continued), pages 50–51

### Preview Pages

Hold up your book, point to each picture and say, *Look at this picture. Look at the caption.* Read each caption aloud as students follow along in their books. Make sure students are looking at the correct picture and caption. Keep vocabulary explanations to a minimum for now, but encourage students to say whatever they can about the pages.

Have the key words (page 43) on the board before the students begin. Read the text or call on individual students to read them aloud. Elicit or explain the meanings of new words, and help students pronounce them. Ask if students found any key words. (pollination, insects) Ask for volunteers to read a couple of sentences containing these words.

Have students read the pages again to themselves. Alternatively, have students read aloud to each other in pairs or small groups.

**Understand Information** Ask comprehension and picture questions such as, *When can the female part of the flower grow into a fruit? What does the fruit protect the seeds from? What are some vegetables that are really fruits? Why are they fruits? What grains are also fruits? Do all seeds grow into new plants? What do most seeds need to grow? Do some seeds need light? How do seeds get moved to other places? What do some fruits stick to? What happens when birds or bats eat fruit?* Continue asking similar questions about all the pictures and the text.

**Organize Information** Have students focus on the pictures on page 50. Ask, *What are some different fruits you see on this page?* Elicit the names of the fruit, write them on the board, and have students write a list in their notebooks. Ask pairs of students to find the names of other fruits in this lesson and add them to their lists. (beans, squash, wheat, oats, coconut, papaya, orange) Check by eliciting the names of the fruits and writing them on the board.

---

**Language Tip:** Plurals: *-es*

Read the text in the Language Tip box aloud or have a volunteer read it to the class. Write these words on the board and have students write them in their notebooks: *tomato* ⟶ *tomatoes, gas* ⟶ *gases.* Ask, *What does* tomato *end with?* (an *o*) Underline the *to* at the end of *tomato.* Say, *For most words ending in a consonant and* o, *we make the plural with* -es. Ask, *What are some other words ending in a consonant and* o? (mango, potato) Write these words on the board. Call on students to spell out the plural forms, and write them on the board. Read all the plural forms aloud. Ask, *Is the plural the /s/ sound or the /z/ sound for these words?* (z) Read the plurals again and have students repeat them. Point to *gas* ⟶ *gases* and ask similar questions.

---

**Science Now**: Growing New Plants

Point to the picture of the scientist. Ask, *What is this scientist doing?* (looking at/observing tomatoes)

Read the text or call on individual students to read it aloud. Elicit or explain the meanings of new words, and help students pronounce them. Write 10 billion in the long form. Have students read the selection again to themselves. Ask comprehension questions such as, *How many people will there be in the world by 2050? When is 2050? How are scientists helping? What's good about these plants?*

Have pairs of students read the first two questions and find the sentences in the text that answer them. Have them write the questions and answers in their notebooks. Check answers before going on.

Answer the third question as a class. Tell students that this is a thinking question. Write student answers on the board and have them copy the answers into their notebooks.

**Answers**
1. Possible answers: Strawberries, tomatoes, grapes, and so on.
2. Wind, water, and animals carry seeds to different places.
3. Possible answers: We plant seeds in the ground. We throw away the seeds in fruit. Some stick to our clothes or shoes. We pass some through our bodies.

## Making New Plants (continued), page 52
## The Plant Life Cycle, page 53

### Preview Pages

Hold up your book, point to the heading, and ask, *What does this say?* Call on individual students to answer. Point to each picture and say, *Look at this picture. Look at the caption.* Read each caption aloud as students follow along in their books. Make sure students are looking at the correct picture and caption. Keep vocabulary explanations to a minimum for now, but encourage students to say whatever they can about the pages.

### Teach Pages

Have the key words (page 43) on the board before students begin. Read the text aloud or call on individual students to read them. Elicit or explain the meanings of new words, and help students pronounce them.

Ask if students found any key words. (germination, insects, pollinate/pollination) Ask for volunteers to read a couple of sentences containing these words.

Have students read the pages again to themselves. Alternatively, have students read aloud to each other in pairs or small groups.

**Understand Information** Ask comprehension and picture questions such as, *What is inside a seed? What does* stored *mean? What does the new plant need to grow? Does this happen quickly? What happens when the seed takes in water? What happens next? What does the plant break out of? What's this called? What grows first? What grows after that?* Continue asking similar questions about all the pictures and the text.

Draw students' attention to the cycle diagram. Ask, *What kind of diagram is this?* Let students look back at page 45, if necessary. Ask, *Why is it called a cycle diagram?* (the events happen again and again, or repeatedly, in the same order) Point to each phase in the plant life cycle and ask a question about it. Also ask, *What happens next?* several times to elicit the cycle. Have students match each stage in the plant life cycle diagram with a sentence in the text.

**Organize Information** Say, *Let's make a sequence diagram of how a seed grows.* Model by writing *How a Seed Grows* and drawing five squares on the board. Ask students, *What happens when the seed takes in water?* Encourage students to look at the second paragraph on page 52. Write the answer on the board. Ask, *What happens next?* Have the students copy the diagram into their notebooks and complete it in pairs or in small groups. Check by eliciting information for the other boxes and writing it on the board. The diagram might look like this:

## How a Seed Grows

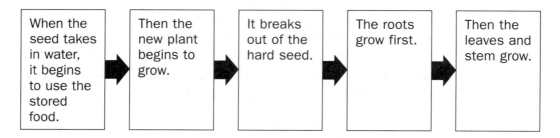

| When the seed takes in water, it begins to use the stored food. | → | Then the new plant begins to grow. | → | It breaks out of the hard seed. | → | The roots grow first. | → | Then the leaves and stem grow. |

---

**Leaders in Science:** George Washington Carver

Point to the picture of peanuts and ask, *What is this?* or *What are these?* Ask, *Who is the man on the stamp? What kind of plant might be on the stamp? What is the name of the science tool on the stamp?*

Read the text and captions aloud, or call on individual students to read them. Elicit or explain the meanings of new words, and help students pronounce them. Have students read the selection again to themselves. Ask comprehension questions such as *When was Carver born? What happened in 1943? Was he a slave in 1943? Who did Carver help? What did he help them to do? Why? What did Carver want farmers to grow? Why? What did Carver think about peanuts? What did he make with them?*

---

**Science at Home:** Uses of Plants

Ask students to look at the title and photograph to predict what the text might be about. Read the text aloud, or call on a student to read it. Elicit or explain the meanings of new words, and help students pronounce them. Ask a few comprehension and critical-thinking questions such as, *What do you need to look around your school or home to find? What are some kinds of foods we eat? What are examples of fruit, grains, and vegetables? What do we build things with? What are some examples? What plant are some clothes made of? Does shampoo have things from plants in it?*

Assign this activity as homework. Tell students to look around their school and homes to find things made from plants. Ask them to make a list in their notebooks.

## Before You Go On

In pairs, have students read the first two questions and find the sentences in the text that answer them. Have them write the questions and answers in their notebooks. Check answers before going on.

Answer the third question together as a class. Tell students that this is a thinking question. Discuss possible answers and write them on the board. Have students copy them into their notebooks.

**Answers**
1. Inside a seed is a new plant and stored food.
2. The roots grow first.
3. Possible answer: The plant will not grow fruit or seeds.

For more information, go to www.longmanusa.com/science for links to interesting websites about plants.

# Review and Practice, pages 54–55

## Vocabulary

If students need help in reviewing the vocabulary, see the Optional Vocabulary Activities (pages vii–viii) and choose an appropriate activity.

Suggest to students that they copy all the sentences into their notebooks before they begin writing the answers. Have students complete this exercise individually. Check answers as a class.

**Answers**
1. pollen
2. photosynthesis
3. Insects
4. energy
5. Pollination
6. germination

## Check Your Understanding

Depending on the language level and abilities of the students, have them answer the questions individually, in pairs, or in small groups. If students need extra support, tell them to look at the information in their notebooks or allow students to look back at the text. Then have students share their answers with the class. Write the answers on the board.

**Answers**
1. During photosynthesis, plants use the energy from sunlight to change water and carbon dioxide into sugar and oxygen.
2. Pollination is pollen passing from the male parts to the female part of a flower.
3. Possible answers: Bananas, papayas, tomatoes, wheat, and apples are fruits.
4. A seed needs water, warmth/heat, nutrients, and (sometimes) light to grow.

## Apply Science Skills

**Science Reading Strategy: Compare and Contrast** Review the science reading strategy. Ask students, *What do we do when we compare and contrast? How does this help us understand?*

Read the instructions aloud, or call on a student to read the instructions. Have students read the page again and copy the diagram into their notebooks. Model by copying the diagram on the board. Elicit one way a papaya and a pinecone are the same and write it on the diagram. Then have students complete the diagram in pairs, in groups, or individually. When they're finished, elicit the information and write it on the board. Answers will vary. The diagram might look like this:

**Papaya**
- fruit
- people eat them
- green outside and orange inside
- soft

**Both**
- have many seeds
- grow on trees
- fall to the ground

**Pinecone**
- cone
- people don't eat them
- brown
- hard

**Using Visuals: Cycle Diagrams** Read the heading and the instructions aloud, or call on individual students to read them. Have students reread silently, if helpful. Ask comprehension questions to review concepts such as, *Do cycle diagrams show the same things happening again and again? What two gases do you see on this diagram? What two living things do you see? What does the tree take in and give off? What does the deer breathe in and breathe out?* If helpful, write these verb phrases on the board: *take in, give off, breathe in, breathe out.*

Allow a few minutes for students to study the cycle diagram. Then have pairs of students ask and answer the questions. Have them write their answers in their notebooks. Check answers as a class.

---

**Answers**
1. Trees give off oxygen. Deer breathe in oxygen and breathe out carbon dioxide. The trees take in the carbon dioxide. Trees need carbon dioxide to live. Deer need oxygen to live.
2. To show a cycle. It shows the process happening again and again.

---

## Discuss

Read the discussion questions aloud. Have students discuss the questions as a class. Encourage them to offer reasons or examples for their opinions.

Workbook pages 27–28 may now be assigned for homework or done in class. These pages provide extra practice in the same categories as the Review and Practice pages in the Student Book.

**44** Unit 1

## Evaluation

### Self-Assessment Questions

Write the following questions on the board. Have students respond in their notebooks. Encourage students to share their responses in small groups or as a class.

1. How can I use compare and contrast to help me in reading?
2. How can cycle diagrams help me understand information?
3. What was difficult for me in this lesson?
4. What was easy for me in this lesson?
5. What was most enjoyable in this lesson?

# Unit Review, pages 56–57

## Warm Up

Have pairs of students list the main ideas from Unit 1. Ask students to use the reading selection headings to group the main ideas. (What is a plant?, parts of a plant, roots, stems, leaves, flowers, how plants work, photosynthesis, making new plants, the plant life cycle) Students may organize the main ideas in a word web.

Ask pairs to exchange their completed lists or word webs. Each pair should review the list or word web to see if any important information is missing. If information is missing, the pair should add it.

Finally, have students contribute information from the lists or word web to a large chart that you make on poster board. Students will use the class chart as a study guide before doing the unit review pages or taking a unit test.

## Vocabulary

With Student Books closed, elicit all the key words and write them on the board. Tell students to use a key word in each answer (point to the key words on the board) and to write full-sentence answers. Model the activity by eliciting the answer for question 1 and writing it on the board. Have students work individually, in pairs, or in small groups, depending on how much support they need. After they have finished, check answers as a class, writing the answers on the board.

### Answers
1. Seeds can grow into new plants.
2. Roots grow in soil.
3. It is called photosynthesis.
4. Energy comes from the sun.
5. The stem holds up a plant.
6. Plants make food in their leaves.
7. It is called germination.
8. Butterflies and bees are insects.
9. The petals of a flower protect the inside parts.
10. The male parts of a flower make pollen.
11. The roots take in water and nutrients from the soil.
12. Pollination takes place.

## Check Your Understanding

Have students work individually, in pairs, or in small groups, depending on how much support they need. After they have finished, check answers as a class, and write the answers on the board.

**Answers**
1. False. Not all/Many/Some plants have broad leaves.
2. True
3. True
4. False. The female part of a flower grows into a fruit.
5. True
6. False. Seeds need water, light, and nutrients to grow.

## Extension Project

Bring in one or more flowers to the class. The flower(s) should have easily identifiable male and female parts.

Read the instructions aloud, or call on a student to read them. Depending on your resources, have students take apart the flower in pairs, in small groups, or as a class. Have students draw pictures of the different separated parts in their notebooks and write labels next to them such as *petals, male parts, female parts, stems, leaves.* Model the activity by drawing a part on the board and labeling it. When students have finished, call on several students to come to the board to draw and label a part of the flower.

## Apply Science Skills

**Using Visuals: Cycle Diagrams** Read the instructions aloud, or call on a student to read them. Draw a circle on the board and number it 1–4 as a model. Point to the cycle diagram and say, *Look at number 1 on the diagram. What do I label it?* Elicit the answer and write it next to number 1 on the board. Have students complete their cycle diagrams individually, in pairs, or in small groups. Check answers as a class. Ask volunteers to complete your diagram on the board.

**Answers**
1. A flower forms. After pollination, a fruit grows.
2. The fruit falls to the ground.
3. A seed germinates in the ground.
4. The plant grows. Its roots, stem, and leaves get bigger.

## Read More About It

Bring at least one of the suggested books to class. Show the cover and some of the inside pages to students as a preview. Ask students to predict what the book is about. Read an excerpt aloud to the class. Then ask or write several comprehension questions. Read the excerpt again before calling on students to answer. Encourage students to find this or another suggested book in their school library or local bookstore.

Workbook pages 29–30 may now be assigned for homework or done in class. These pages provide extra practice in the same categories that appear in the Unit Review pages in the Student Book.

## Unit Experiment, pages 58–59
### Do Plants Grow toward Light?

### Preview

Begin this section with books closed. Elicit and review the scientific method by asking, *What are the five steps of the scientific method we studied in the Getting Started unit?* Give prompts and hints, if necessary, and write the steps on the board.

### Do the Experiment

For this experiment, you can use seedlings from the beans students sprouted in the Getting Started unit. Alternatively, you can buy seedlings at a garden supply store. Look for seedlings that are fast growing. Depending on your resources, have students do this experiment in pairs, in small groups, or as a class.

Review the relevant safety tips on pages 14–15. Make sure students know how to use scissors correctly and safely, to wash their hands after touching soil, and to clean up any spills right away.

Call on a student to read the experiment title. Tell students, *This is our main question.* Read aloud the introduction, purpose, and materials, or have individual students read them.

Workbook page 31 should be used to record the steps during the experiment.

On the board, point to *Make a hypothesis.* Ask, *What is our hypothesis? Do you think plants grow toward the light? Raise your hand if you think so.* If this is the majority, say, *This is our hypothesis.* Write the hypothesis on the board while students write it in their Experiment Logs. Ask, *What do we do next?* (test the hypothesis) Tell students, *Next we'll observe the plant growing. We'll write down our observations. Then we'll draw conclusions.*

Read the What to Do instructions aloud, or have a student read them. Ask comprehension questions to be sure students know what to do. Be sure to ask if they have any questions. Then have students perform each step. After steps 4 and 6, and after watering, have students place the lid on the shoebox so that the plant will have only one source of light.

When the experiment has been completed, elicit conclusions and have students add the information to their logs.

Workbook page 32 may now be assigned for homework or done in class. This page provides writing practice and an opportunity for students to relate their personal experience to the unit content.

# Unit 2 Animals
## Unit Overview

| Lesson | Content | Science Skills | | Experiment |
| | | Reading Strategies | Using Visuals | |
|---|---|---|---|---|
| 1 | • What Is an Animal?<br>• What Animals Need<br>• Animal Adaptations | Use What You Know | Photographs | What Traits Do Animals Share? |
| 2 | • Kinds of Animals<br>• Fish, Amphibians, Reptiles, Birds, Mammals | Key Sentences | Pie Charts | |

## Objectives

**Vocabulary**
- Develop new vocabulary related to animals
- Use newly acquired vocabulary in context

**Concepts**
- Learn about animal traits
- Learn about vertebrates and invertebrates
- Learn about the five basic groups of vertebrates

**Reading Strategies**
- Use what you know to understand what you read
- Recognize key sentences in a paragraph
- Practice previously learned strategies

**Using Visuals**
- Understand how to study photographs for information
- Understand how to study pie charts for information

**Experiment**
- Identify what animals have in common

## Unit Opener, pages 60–61

### Preview Topic

Ask students to preview the pages. Give students a few moments. Then ask, *What is this unit about? What do you think you'll learn about animals?*

Ask students what they see in the pictures. Encourage them to say whatever they can. Point to each picture and give a little more information about it.

### Unit Concepts

Read aloud the list of unit concepts for Lesson 1. Ask, *What words do you know here?* Write any words students know on the board. Ask students what the words mean. Tell students they will learn the other words as they read the lessons.

### Get Ready

Bring in a plant and a stuffed animal to show to the class. Identify both as living things. Ask, *What do you know about plants?* Elicit information about plants that students learned in Unit 1. If necessary, ask specific questions from the unit.

Hold up the stuffed animal. Tell students it represents all animals. Ask, *What do you know about animals?* Elicit as much information as possible.

Draw students' attention to the Venn diagram. Ask, *What kind of diagram is this? When did we make one before?*

Read the instructions aloud, or call on individual students to read them. Tell students to copy the diagram into their notebooks while you draw it on the board. Call on volunteers to name one fact about plants that you can write under *Plants*. Do the same with *Animals*. Point to the space in the middle labeled *Both*. Ask, *What do both plants and animals share?* Again, call on volunteers to answer or prompt students with clues, if necessary. Students might not have too many ideas right now, but you can go back to this diagram at the end of the unit and see what they can add.

The Venn diagram might look like this:

**Plants**
- make their own food
- can't move from the ground
- have roots in the soil
- have flowers, leaves, stems
- need carbon dioxide
- make seeds and fruit
- are quiet

**Both**
- are living things
- need water
- live on Earth
- there are different kinds
- grow

**Animals**
- eat food
- can move
- have bodies
- need oxygen
- have babies
- make sounds

# Lesson ❶

## Before You Read, pages 62–65

Hold up your book and ask students, *What are the headings? What do you see in the pictures? What will you learn in this lesson?*

### Vocabulary

Read the captions aloud, or call on students to read them. Help students understand and pronounce new words. Use pictures, props, and mime. Have students read the captions again silently or with a partner. Ask picture and comprehension questions for each item.

Read the key words (page 63) aloud and have students say them after you. Say, *These words are important in this lesson. These words will help you understand the lesson.*

### Practice

Have students write the sentences in their notebooks, leaving a space for each answer. Model completing the first sentence with the class, if necessary.

Individually or in pairs, have students choose the correct answers and write them in the sentences. Check answers by calling on individual students. Write the letters of the correct answers on the board.

> **Answers**
> **1.** a. survive     **3.** b. herbivore     **5.** b. traits
> **2.** c. omnivore     **4.** b. carnivore     **6.** a. species

Workbook page 33 may now be assigned.

### Science Skills

**Science Reading Strategy: Use What You Know** With books closed, write *Use What You Know* on the board. Tell students, *When you read, think about the topic. Think about what you already know about it. Use what you know to help you understand.* Ask students, *What topic are we studying in this unit?* (animals) Write *Animals* on the board and draw a circle around it. Tell students, *This is the topic. What do you know about animals? You know some animal names. You know some kinds of animals.* Begin drawing a word web on the board. Make a smaller circle connected to the *Animals* circle with a line and write *kinds*. Tell students, *I know birds are animals.* Draw a line from the *kinds* circle to a smaller circle and write *birds*. Ask, *What are some other animals?* Elicit the names of two or three other animals and add them to the word web on the board.

Have students open their books to page 64. Read the information aloud, or call on individual students to read it. Have students reread it silently, if helpful. Have students look at the Use What You Know word web. Point out that this is called a *word web*. Point out that *homes* are where animals live; for example, a fish lives in water. Ask students to copy the word web into their notebooks.

Elicit information for each of the other branches. Write it on the board and have students add it to their word webs. Remind students to use the Use What You Know strategy as they read.

Workbook page 34 may now be assigned.

**Using Visuals: Photographs**  Have students look back at pages 62 and 63. Hold up your book and point to the picture of the lions on page 62. Say, *This is a photograph. Photographs give us information.* Ask, *What are the lions eating?* (other animals, or meat) Point to the picture of the elephant. Ask, *What is the elephant eating?* (plants) *What else do you see in the pictures? What animals have a lot of hair?* (the lions, the bear, the tarantula) Tell students, *These photographs give us a lot of information.*

Have students read the heading at the top of page 65. Ask students, *What visuals did you learn about in Unit 1?* (diagrams, cycle diagrams) *What visual will you practice using in this lesson?*

Read the introduction aloud, or call on individual students to read it. Help students pronounce the new animal names.

Have students study the photos for a few minutes. Then have pairs of students ask and answer the first two questions. Have them write their answers in their notebooks. Check answers before moving on to question 3.

Answer the third question together as a class. Elicit as much information as possible. Ask questions to elicit more answers, if needed. Write the answers on the board and have students copy them into their notebooks.

---

**Answers**

1. The otter and praying mantis eat other animals.
2. The horse and silkworm eat plants.
3. Possible answers: The horse is eating flowers. The otter is eating a fish. The otter is wet. The silkworm is eating a leaf. The silkworm has many legs. The praying mantis is eating another insect. The horse, otter, and silkworm have hair.

---

Workbook pages 35–36 may now be assigned.

# Lesson ①

---

## What Is an Animal? pages 66–67

---

### Preview Pages

Call students' attention to the heading, pictures, and captions before reading. Allow students to say whatever they can about the pictures and captions. Keep vocabulary explanations to a minimum for now.

### Teach Pages

Read the text and the captions aloud, or call on individual students to read them.

Help students with new words. Elicit any key words (species, traits), the sentences they are in, and their definitions. Have students read the pages again to themselves. Alternatively, have students read aloud to each other in pairs or small groups.

**Understand Information** Ask comprehension and picture questions such as, *How many kingdoms of living things are there? Is the animal kingdom very large? Are there many species of animals? What makes each species different? What do animals do that plants don't do? How do animals get from place to place? Can animals make food the way plants do? What do animals need to do to get food? What kind of plants do animals find? How do animals get meat? What do animals have to get away from? What's an example of this?* Continue asking similar questions about all the pictures and the text.

**Organize Information** As a class, make a chart showing the main idea and details for page 67. Ask students, *What's the main idea on this page?* If needed, ask, *What do animals do that plants don't?* (Animals move.) Ask students, *What are the details on this page? Why do animals move?* Elicit the details from students, asking specific questions, if needed. Write this information on the board in a Main Idea and Details chart and have students copy it into their notebooks.

## Optional Activity

Have students learn the names of animals in this unit. As you proceed through the unit, students can list the animals on each page. Later, students can write the names on index cards and categorize them in different ways.

---

**HISTORY CONNECTION: Naming Species**

Ask students to look at the title and photograph to predict what the text might be about. Say, *Remember that we can use photographs to get information. What information is in this photograph? What species is this? How do you think species get their names?* Read the text aloud, or call on a student to read it. Check understanding and pronunciation of new words. Have students reread silently, if helpful. Ask comprehension questions. For a possible research project, have students find other species named after people.

---

**Language Tip: Lion/Lioness**

Have students look at the picture on page 67 and point to the word *lioness*. Write *lion/lioness* on the board. Ask, *What letters are different in these two words?* (-ess) Point to the Language Tip on page 67 and say, *We use* lion *to mean a male lion and* lioness *to mean a female lion.* If students do not understand *male* and *female* (which they learned in Unit 1), point to several different students and say, *male student* or *female student* until students understand.

**Before You Go On**

Have pairs of students answer the first two questions. Have them write the questions and answers in their notebooks. Check answers before going on. Answer the third question together as a class.

**Answers**
1. Unlike plants, animals move around. They swim, walk, run, or fly.
2. Animals need to move to get food. Animals also move to get away from danger.
3. The animal will not survive. It will not live.

## What Animals Need, pages 68–69

### Preview Pages

Call students' attention to the heading, pictures, and captions before reading. Allow students to say whatever they can about the pictures and captions. Keep vocabulary explanations to a minimum for now.

### Teach Pages

Read the text and the captions aloud, or call on individual students to read them. Help students with new words. Elicit the key word (survive), the sentence it is in, and the definition. Have students read the pages again to themselves. Alternatively, have students read aloud to each other in pairs or small groups.

**Understand Information** Ask picture and comprehension questions such as, *What happens when an animal can't find oxygen, water, food, and shelter? How do animals breathe on land? How do gills help fish? How do whales get a breath of air? What is an animal's body mostly made of? How do we get water? How do other animals get most of their water?* Continue asking similar questions about all the pictures and the text.

**Organize Information** Draw a graphic organizer like the one below. In the center, write *What Animals Need*. Say to students, *There are four things animals need. What's one thing?* Write the answer on the board on one arm of the graphic. Have students copy this graphic into their notebooks. Tell them to complete the graphic by writing the other three things animals need. The completed graphic might look like this:

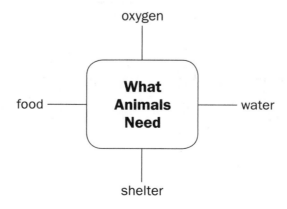

## Language Tip: Breathe/Breath

Have students find the sentences on page 68 that contain *breathe* and *breath*. Write the sentences on the board, underlining the two words. Model the pronunciation of *breathe* and *breath* and have students repeat them. Contrast the long vowel sound in *breathe* and the short vowel sound in *breath*. Demonstrate breathing. Then demonstrate a breath. Explain that there are many words in English that look similar or the same in the verb and the noun form. Check that students know the difference between a verb and a noun. Write new verb/noun examples on the board that can be found on other pages in this unit. (to need/a need, to drink/a drink, to live/a life, to help/a help) Encourage students to make sentences using these verb and noun form examples.

## Science Now: Taking Salt Out of Seawater

Ask students to look at the title and photograph to predict what the text might be about.

Read the text and the captions aloud, or call on individual students to read them. Elicit or explain the meanings of new words. Use props (salt, a glass of fresh water) and pictures (steam, seawater) to help with comprehension. Have students read the paragraph again to themselves. Ask comprehension questions such as, *What do some countries not have enough of? What have scientists learned to do? Why is the water heated? Does the steam have salt in it? What happens as the steam is cooled? Is there salt in the water now?*

To make sure students understand this process, draw a simple diagram on the board like the one below. Next to the diagram, make a list of labels: *Fresh water, Seawater, Steam, The water is now salt-free, The steam changes to water, Seawater is heated to make steam.* Elicit where the first two labels go and write them on the board. Pair students and have them copy and complete the diagram in their notebooks.

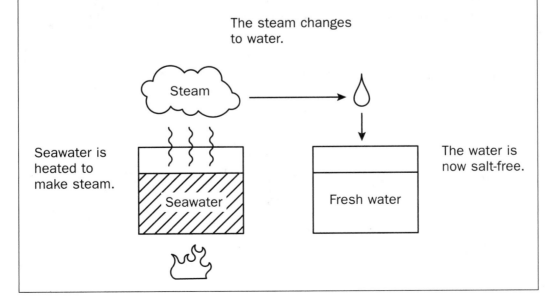

The steam changes to water.

Steam

Seawater is heated to make steam.

Seawater

The water is now salt-free.

Fresh water

**Before You Go On**

Have pairs of students answer the first two questions. Have them write the questions and answers in their notebooks. Check answers before going on. Answer the third question together as a class.

**Answers**
1. All animals need oxygen, water, food, and shelter.
2. Animals that live on land just breathe in the air to get oxygen. Gills help fish get oxygen from the water. Whales have to come up to the top of the water to get a breath of air.
3. Possible answers: Fruits and vegetables. Animals also contain a lot of water.

## What Animals Need (continued), pages 70–71

### Preview Pages

Call students' attention to the pictures and captions before reading. Allow students to say whatever they can about them. Keep vocabulary explanations to a minimum for now.

### Teach Pages

Read the text and the captions aloud, or call on individual students to read them. Help students with new words. Elicit any key words (carnivore, herbivore, omnivore), the sentences they are in, and their definitions. Have students read the pages again to themselves. Alternatively, have students read aloud to each other in pairs or small groups.

**Understand Information** Ask comprehension and picture questions such as, *What kind of animals are lions, frogs, and tarantulas? What do they eat? How do most carnivores get their food? Can frogs run fast? How do frogs get their food? What are cows and horses? What do they eat? What are bears and humans? What do we eat?* Continue asking similar questions about all the pictures and the text.

**Organize Information** Have students make word webs showing the three types of animals—carnivores, herbivores, and omnivores—and examples of each type. Model this activity by starting the webs on the board. Have students copy the webs into their notebooks and complete them with as many examples as they can. Encourage students to look for information in their books. The webs might look like this:

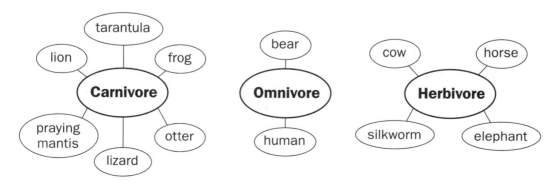

## Science at Home: What Do We Eat?

Ask students to predict what the text might be about. Say, *What information is in this photograph?*

Read the text aloud, or call on a student to read it. Draw a T-chart on the board with the heading *Foods We Eat* and the categories *Plants* and *Animals*. Have students begin the same T-chart in their notebooks. Pantomime looking in your kitchen cabinets or refrigerator to see what is inside. Write a few food items in the chart. Tell students that for homework they need to write at least six items in their charts.

Review students' completed charts the next day. Have students raise their hands if they had (1) more animal products, (2) more plant products, or (3) the same number of plant and animal products in their charts.

## As You Read: Use What You Know

Read the text in the As You Read box aloud, or call on a student to read it. Point to the pictures of the nest and beaver lodge. Say, *Use what you know. What do you know about animal shelters, or homes? Where are they?* (on land, in trees, in the soil, underwater, and so on) *What are they made of?* (wood/trees, rock, grass, leaves, other plants) *What do the animals do in them?* (sleep, eat, rest, take care of babies, keep warm, get away from danger) Say, *Remember to use what you know as you read.*

## Before You Go On

Have pairs of students answer the first two questions. Have them write the questions and answers in their notebooks. Check answers before going on. Answer the third question together as a class.

**Answers**
1. Animals get energy from food.
2. Animals need a place to rest. Shelters keep an animal warm and dry. They keep an animal cool when it is hot outside. Animals can hide from other animals in a shelter. It is a place to have babies and keep them safe.
3. Possible answers: In my shelter I play, watch TV, study, sleep, eat, rest, talk with my family, keep warm or cool, keep dry, keep safe.

# Exploring, page 72

## Preview Page

Call students' attention to the heading, pictures, and captions before reading. Allow students to say whatever they can about the pictures and captions. Ask if they recognize any birds on the page. If so, they can use what they know to think about the birds before reading. Remind them that this is a special page in each unit. Keep vocabulary explanations to a minimum for now.

Read the text aloud, or call on individual students to read it. Help students with new words. Have students read the page again to themselves. Alternatively, have students read aloud to each other in pairs or small groups.

**Understand Information** Ask comprehension and picture questions such as, *What do cardinals eat? What kind of beak do they have?* or *What kind of bird has a sharp, hooked beak? What do hawks eat?* Continue asking similar questions about all the pictures and the text.

Ask critical-thinking questions such as, *How does a woodpecker's beak help it eat?* (It can put its beak deep inside a tree.) *How does a pelican's beak help it eat?* (It can catch fish.) *How about a hawk's beak?* (It can kill small animals.) *And a cardinal's beak?* (It can get seeds easily.)

**Organize Information** Have students draw a picture of the head and beak of each bird in their notebooks. Have them label each picture with the name of the bird, the type of food it eats, and its beak shape.

## Animal Adaptations, page 73

**Preview Page**

Call students' attention to the heading, pictures, and captions before reading. Allow students to say whatever they can about the pictures and captions. Keep vocabulary explanations to a minimum for now.

Ask students what they already know about traits such as a bird's beak. Brainstorm a list of different traits on the board. Then tell students that they are going to learn about other traits.

**Teach Page**

Read the text and captions aloud, or call on individual students to read them. Help students with new words. Elicit any key words (trait, herbivore, carnivore), the sentences they are in, and their definitions. Have students read the page again to themselves. Alternatively, have students read aloud to each other in pairs or small groups.

**Understand Information** Ask comprehension and picture questions such as, *What do adaptations help animals do? What's a good example of an adaptation? What do different types of teeth allow animals to do? What kind of teeth do herbivores have? How do they use their teeth? What kind of teeth do carnivores have? How do they use their teeth? Is the shape of an animal's teeth a trait?* Continue asking similar questions about both pictures and the text.

**Organize Information** Have students make a word web showing examples of traits. Draw an oval on the board and write *Traits* in it. Ask, *What's an example of a trait?* Draw a line from the oval to a smaller circle and write the answer inside it.

Elicit another example. Have pairs or small groups of students copy the web into their notebooks and complete it with as many examples as they can. Encourage them to add human traits that the class talked about. The web might look like this:

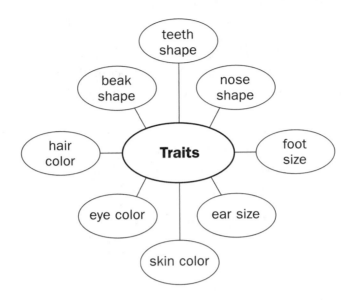

---

**Language Tip:** *Possessive* s

Review the use of *s* to show possession. Point to a student's book and write (*Juan's*) *science book.* Say, *This book belongs to* (*Juan*). *This is* (*Juan's*) *book.* Model another example of possession or ask a student to give you an example. Write it on the board. Continue with more examples until students understand. Then point to all the books on the desks and say, *These books belong to the students. These are the students' books.* Write *students' books* on the board. Circle the apostrophe + *s* in *Juan's* and the *s* + apostrophe in *students'*. Ask, *What is different here?* Elicit that when the owner or possessor is plural, you place the apostrophe <u>after</u> the *s*. If the owner is singular, you place the apostrophe <u>before</u> the *s*. Call on a volunteer to read the Language Tip. Ask students to think of additional examples using singular and plural possession.

---

## REACHING ALL STUDENTS: Kinesthetic Learners

Make a list on the board of the new action-word vocabulary from this lesson (*catch, get away from, chase, breathe in, hide, bite, chew, tear*). Have students stand. Say and pantomime each word, and have students mimic you. When you think students know the words, say them randomly, without miming them yourself, and have students act them out.

Have pairs of students answer the first two questions. Have them write the questions and answers in their notebooks. Check answers before going on. Answer the third question together as a class.

**Answers**
1. An example of an adaptation is the difference between the teeth of an herbivore and the teeth of a carnivore.
2. An herbivore has flat teeth. A carnivore has sharp teeth.
3. Possible answers: teeth shape, nose shape, mouth shape, foot size, ear size, height, straight or curly hair.

For more information, go to www.longmanusa.com/science for links to interesting websites about animals.

# Review and Practice, pages 74–75

## Vocabulary

If students need help reviewing the vocabulary, see the Optional Vocabulary Activities (pages vii–viii). Have students complete the exercise individually. Check answers as a class.

**Answers**

| | | |
|---|---|---|
| 1. survive | 3. carnivore | 5. trait |
| 2. herbivore | 4. omnivore | 6. species |

## Check Your Understanding

Have students answer the questions individually, in pairs, or in small groups. If students need extra support, tell them to look at the information in their notebooks or allow students to look back at the text. Then have students share their answers with the class. Write the answers on the board.

**Answers**
1. Animals need to move to get food. Animals also move to get away from danger.
2. An animal needs oxygen, water, food, and shelter to survive.
3. A shelter is a place to rest. It keeps an animal warm and dry. It keeps an animal cool when it is hot outside. It can be a place to hide from other animals. It is a place to have babies and keep them safe.
4. An example of an adaptation is teeth shape or beak shape.

## Apply Science Skills

**Science Reading Strategy: Use What You Know** Review the reading strategy first. Then read the instructions aloud, or call on a student to read them.

Copy the word web on the board. Elicit several kinds of mammals and write them in the web. Then elicit information for the other branches of the web. Encourage students to guess. The completed web might look like this:

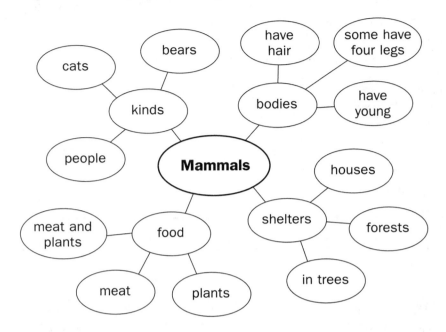

**Using Visuals: Photographs** Tell students, *You learned a lot using the photographs in this lesson. These photographs will show you some new information.* Read the instructions aloud, or call on individual students to read them. Help students pronounce the new animal names. (gorilla, wolf) Have students reread silently, if helpful.

Allow a few minutes for students to study the photos. Then have pairs ask and answer the first two questions. Answer the third question together as a class. Elicit as many answers to question 3 as possible.

---

**Answers**
1. The beaver and zebra have herbivore teeth. The wolf and tiger have carnivore teeth.
2. The gorilla and human have both types of teeth.
3. Possible answers: You can see fur, hair, noses, eyes, skin color, and ears.

---

## Discuss

Check for comprehension of the word *zoo*. Have students discuss the question as a class. Encourage them to offer reasons for or against zoos and to give examples.

 Workbook pages 37–38 may now be assigned.

## Evaluation

### Self-Assessment Questions

Write the following questions on the board. Have students respond in their notebooks. Encourage students to share their responses in small groups or as a class.

1. How can I use what I know to help me in reading?
2. How can photographs help me understand new ideas?
3. What was difficult for me in this lesson?
4. What was easy for me in this lesson?
5. What was most enjoyable in this lesson?

# Lesson ❷

## Before You Read, pages 76–79

Hold up your book and ask students, *What are the headings? What do you see in the pictures? What will you learn in this lesson?*

## Vocabulary

Read the captions aloud, or call on students to read them. Help students understand and pronounce new words. Use pictures, props, and mime. Have students read the captions again silently. Ask picture and comprehension questions for each item.

Practice the compare-and-contrast reading strategy from Lesson 1 to help students understand the content on these pages. Ask, *How are the animals on these pages the same?* (The dog and human are mammals. They both have hair or fur. They both give their young milk, and so on.) Ask, *How are these animals different?* (The dog has fur and the human has hair, and so on.)

Read the key words (page 77) aloud and have students say them after you. Say, *These words are important in this lesson. These words will help you understand the lesson.*

## Practice

Read the instructions and the example aloud. Have students copy the example definition into their notebooks. Have students define the other words in pairs or in small groups. Check answers by calling on individual students. Write their definitions on the board, correcting as necessary.

---

**Possible Answers**
- amphibians: animals that begin life in the water and later live on land
- invertebrates: animals without backbones
- mammals: animals that have fur or hair; animals that give milk to their young
- reptiles: animals that have bodies covered with scales or plates
- vertebrates: animals with backbones

---

 Workbook page 39 may now be assigned.

## Science Skills

Use a Strategy**Science Reading Strategy: Key Sentences** Begin this practice with books closed. Write the heading *Key Sentences* on the board. Underneath write, *Humans have hair. Some have black hair, and some have brown hair. Humans are mammals.* Tell students, *When you read, look for the most important sentences. Look for key sentences.* Ask students, *What are the two key sentences here?* (Humans have hair. Humans are mammals.) Ask, *What sentence isn't so important?* (Some have black hair, and some have brown hair.) Circle *Some* and tell students, *Sentences with* some *often give details but not the main ideas.* Circle the key sentences. Say, *These two sentences tell main facts about humans. They tell what all humans have or do.*

Have students open their books to page 78. Read the introduction aloud, or call on individual students to read it. Have students reread it silently, if helpful.

Read the paragraph and captions aloud. Elicit or explain the meanings of new words, and help students pronounce them.

Have students look at the key sentences chart. Point out that it shows information with the math signs = (equals) and + (plus). Say, *This graphic shows the key sentences about what all arthropods have or do.* Read the key sentences aloud, or call on individual students to read them. Ask students to copy the chart into their notebooks.

Ask comprehension questions such as, *Are the arthropods a small group in the animal kingdom? What are examples of arthropods? What kind of bodies do all arthropods have? Do arthropods have bones? Is the outside of their bodies soft? What does the outside of their bodies protect? Are all arthropods large?*

WorkbookWorkbook page 40 may now be assigned.

**Using Visuals: Pie Charts** Draw a picture of a pie on the board, or show students a picture of a whole pie. Say, *This is a pie. Did anyone eat any of this pie?* (no) *Is it a whole pie?* (yes) Write on the board: *Whole = 100 percent (%).* Draw a circle on the board. Say, *This is a pie chart. It looks like a pie. It equals 100 percent, too.* Draw a line down the center of the pie. Point to one half and ask, *How big is this piece of pie?* (1/2) Write one-half on the board as a fraction and in words. Ask, *What percent is one-half of 100 percent?* (50 percent) Show the equation *50 + 50 = 100*, if necessary. Write *50%* in the chart. Draw a line bisecting the other half. Ask, *How big is this piece of pie?* (1/4) Write one-fourth on the board as a fraction and in words. Ask, *What percent is one-fourth of 100 percent?* (25 percent) Write *25%* in the chart, showing the equation *25 + 25 + 25 + 25 = 100*, if necessary. Sum up by pointing to the different pieces on the pie chart and asking, *What percent is this?* Say, *A pie chart shows us parts of a whole.*

Have students read the heading at the top of the page. Ask students, *What visuals did you learn about in other lessons?* (diagrams, cycle diagrams, photographs) *What visual will you practice using in this lesson?*

Read aloud the information at the top of page 79, or call on individual students to read it. Help students understand and pronounce new words. Have students reread silently, if helpful.

Allow students to study the chart for a few minutes. Then have students ask and answer the questions in pairs. Have them write their answers in their notebooks.

If students are having trouble with question 2, write *100 – 82 = ?* on the board.
Check answers as a class. Write the correct answers on the board.

---

**Answers**
1. 82% of species in the animal kingdom are arthropods.
2. 18% are not arthropods.
3. Some examples of arthropods are crabs, butterflies, spiders, ants, and scorpions.

---

 Workbook pages 41–42 may now be assigned.

## Lesson ❷

## Kinds of Animals, pages 80–81

### Preview Pages

Call students' attention to the heading, pictures, and captions before reading. Allow students to say whatever they can about the pictures and captions. Keep vocabulary explanations to a minimum for now.

### Teach Pages

Read the text and the captions aloud, or call on individual students to read them. Help students with new words. Elicit any key words (vertebrates, invertebrates, amphibians, reptiles, mammals), the sentences they are in, and their definitions. Have students read the pages again to themselves. Alternatively, have students read aloud to each other in pairs or small groups.

**Understand Information** Ask picture and comprehension questions such as, *How many species of animals do scientists know of? How many groups do scientists divide these animals into? What are they? What are examples of vertebrates? What are examples of invertebrates? What don't invertebrates have? Do they have any bones?* Continue asking similar questions about the pictures and the text.

Have students focus on the pie chart. Ask, *What is the title of this pie chart?* Point to the percentages and ask, *What is 95% plus 5%?* Say, *This pie chart shows the whole animal kingdom.* Ask, *What percent of the animal kingdom are invertebrates? What are some examples of invertebrates on this page? What percent of the animal kingdom are vertebrates? Does this surprise you? What's an example of a vertebrate on this page?*

**Organize Information** Have students make a word web showing the two main groups in the animal kingdom and the five kinds of vertebrates. Write *The Animal Kingdom* on the board and draw an oval around it. Ask, *What are the two main kinds of animals?* Draw two lines from the *Animal Kingdom* oval and write their answers in two new ovals, *Vertebrates* and *Invertebrates.* Say, *There are five kinds of vertebrates,* and draw five lines from the *Vertebrate* oval. Ask, *What's one kind?* Write this answer on the board. Have students copy the web into their notebooks and complete it individually.

The completed web might look like this:

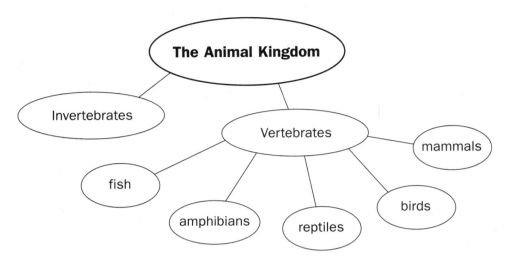

---

**Language Tip:** Prefix *in-*

Write *Invertebrate* and *Vertebrate* on the board. Ask for the definition of each word and write the definitions on the board next to the words. (Elicit *not* as part of the definition of invertebrate: does <u>not</u> have a backbone.) Underline *in* in the word <u>*in*</u>*vertebrate* and <u>*not*</u> in the definition. Say, *In is a prefix. We attach it to words to give them an opposite meaning. The prefix* in *means "no or not."* Give other examples, such as *action/inaction, attention/inattention, complete/incomplete, correct/incorrect.* Tell students to look for this prefix as they read to help them understand the meanings of words.

---

## Optional Activity

Have students look through Lesson 1 to find animals that are vertebrates or invertebrates. Ask students to write the names of the animals in a T-chart labeled *Vertebrate / Invertebrate.*

### Before You Go On

Have pairs of students answer the first two questions. Have them write the questions and answers in their notebooks. Check answers before going on. Answer the third question together as a class.

**Answers**
1. The two main groups of animals are vertebrates and invertebrates.
2. 5% of animal species have backbones.
3. My/Your backbone is in the middle of my/your back. Possible answers: Bones in my/your head/chest/hips/ribs protect my/your inner parts.

# Fish, page 82
# Amphibians, page 83

**Preview Pages**

Call students' attention to the headings, pictures, and captions before reading. Allow students to say whatever they can about the pictures and captions. Keep vocabulary explanations to a minimum for now.

**Teach Pages**

Read the text and captions aloud, or call on individual students to read them. Help students with new words. Elicit the key word (amphibian), the sentence it is in, and the definition. Have students read the pages again to themselves. Alternatively, have students read aloud to each other in pairs or small groups.

**Understand Information** Ask picture and comprehension questions such as, *Where do some fish live? Where do others live? What do fish usually have on their bodies? Can you point to scales in the picture? Do most fish grow inside their mother's body? Do all sharks hatch from eggs? Do amphibians grow inside their mother's body?* Continue asking similar questions about all the pictures and the text.

Use the illustration of the stages in a frog's life to elicit facts about amphibians. Remind students about cycles from Unit 1. Say, *This picture shows the life cycle of a frog.* Point to the eggs. Say, *The eggs are the first stage.* Point to the next stage and ask, *What happens next?* Continue asking about each stage in the life cycle.

**As You Read:** Key Sentences

Read the instructions aloud or call on a student to read them. Remind students to find sentences about traits all or most fish have. You may wish to have students work in pairs or individually to find the key sentences on page 82. (Fish live in water all over the earth. Fish's bodies are adapted for life in the water. All fish have gills to take in oxygen. They also have fins on the outside of their bodies. Almost all fish hatch from eggs.) Check answers as a class.

**Organize Information** Point to the As You Read box on page 82. Have students make a key-sentences chart for fish. Go back to the chart on page 78 to remind students what it looks like. Draw a square on the board and write *Fish* inside. Draw an equal sign and ask, *How many key sentences did we find about fish?* (five) Draw five boxes with plus signs between them. Ask, *What's the first key sentence?* (Fish live in water all over the earth.) Write *live in water* in the first box. Have the students copy this chart into their notebooks and complete it in pairs or in small groups. Check answers as a class. The chart might look like this:

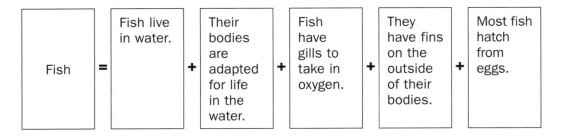

| Fish | = | | + | Their bodies are adapted for life in the water. | + | Fish have gills to take in oxygen. | + | They have fins on the outside of their bodies. | + | Most fish hatch from eggs. |

Fish = Fish live in water. + Their bodies are adapted for life in the water. + Fish have gills to take in oxygen. + They have fins on the outside of their bodies. + Most fish hatch from eggs.

---

**Language Tip:** Pronunciation: *ph = f* sound

Read the text in the Language Tip box aloud or have a volunteer read it to the class. Write on the board *ph = /f/*. Explain that the letters *ph* in English are most often pronounced like the sound of the letter *f*. Write *amphibian* on the board and underline *ph*. Help students pronounce it correctly. Ask, *Are there any other words in this unit that begin with* ph *or have those letters?* (photographs, photos, dolphins) Encourage students to look through previous pages to find words. Write the words on the board and underline *ph*. Again, help with pronunciation.

Finally, ask students if they can use what they know to think of other words that contain *ph*. (pharmacy, graph, geography, phylum, physical, phrase, and so on) Alternatively, have students look in a dictionary under *ph* to see how many words begin with the letters.

---

## REACHING ALL STUDENTS: Visual and Kinesthetic Learners

Draw simple pictures on the board of a fish, a tadpole, and a frog (with lungs shown). Have students draw them in their notebooks. Alternatively, prepare handouts. Tell students to label the body parts they studied. Model by pointing to the fish's gill and asking, *What is this?* Draw a line from the gill and write *gill*. Have students complete their diagrams individually. Then ask for volunteers to label them on the board. The finished diagrams might look like this:

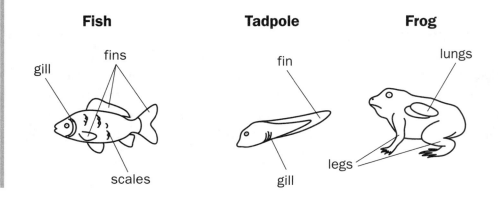

**Fish**  |  **Tadpole**  |  **Frog**

fins
gill
scales

fin
gill

lungs
legs

**Before You Go On**

Have pairs of students answer the first two questions. Have them write the questions and answers in their notebooks. Check answers before going on. Answer the third question together as a class.

**Answers**
1. Fish use fins to move.
2. Fish have gills to take in oxygen.
3. Amphibians use their gills and fins to survive in water. They use their lungs and legs to survive on land.

# Reptiles, page 84
# Birds, page 85

## Preview Pages

Call students' attention to the headings, pictures, and captions before reading. Allow students to say whatever they can about the pictures and captions. Keep vocabulary explanations to a minimum for now.

## Teach Pages

Read the text and the captions aloud, or call on individual students to read them. Help students with new words. Elicit the key word (reptiles), the sentence it is in, and the definition. Have students read the pages again to themselves. Alternatively, have students read aloud to each other in pairs or small groups.

**Understand Information**  Ask picture and comprehension questions such as, *Where do most reptiles live? What protects reptiles' inner parts? Do most reptiles grow inside their mothers' bodies? Where do sea turtles leave their eggs? What do the sea turtles do after that? Where do birds live? Can all birds fly? Do all birds hatch from eggs? What else do they all do? Do all birds have wings? What bird can't fly?* Continue asking similar questions about all the pictures and the text.

**Organize Information**  Have students make a T-chart showing what all birds have or do and what some birds have or do. Model by drawing a T-chart on the board with the categories *All birds* and *Most/Some/A few birds.* Say, *Look at page 85. What can I write under* All birds? (hatch from eggs) *What can I write under* Most/Some/A few birds? (most fly) Depending on the level of your students, either elicit a few more items for the chart or have pairs or small groups complete the chart. Check answers as a class. Have volunteers fill in the chart on the board.

## Science at Home: Reptiles at the Zoo

Draw students' attention to the picture of the snake. Ask, *What do you already know about snakes?* Write student responses on the board. Read the caption, *Anaconda*. Ask if anyone knows about anacondas. Read the title and text aloud or have a volunteer read it to the class. Demonstrate 250 kilograms (550 lbs) by grouping together four or five students and saying that together they weigh about 250 kilograms. Ask comprehension questions such as, *What snake is very interesting? How much does it weigh? Is it the heaviest snake in the world?* Encourage students to look for more information about anacondas and other snakes.

## Environment Watch: Endangered Species

Point to the picture of the parrot. Ask, *Does anyone know what kind of bird this is?* Encourage students to make guesses.

Read the text aloud, or call on individual students to read it. Elicit or explain the meanings of new words. Have students read the selection again to themselves. Ask comprehension questions.

Point out other animals that are endangered, letting students look at the pictures of these animals again: the leatherback sea turtle shown laying eggs (page 84); the gray wolf (page 75); the orangutan (page 67); the mountain gorilla (page 6). The brown bear (page 62) and the polar bear (page 86) are also in danger. You may wish to download photos of other endangered species.

Discuss endangered species with the class. Ask, *How do you feel about these animals? What can humans do to help them?* (stop cutting down forests, stop hunting the animals)

## Before You Go On

Have students read the first two questions. Have pairs of students find the sentences in the text that answer them. Have them write the questions and answers in their notebooks. Check answers before going on.

Answer the third question together as a class. Tell students they need to look for key sentences to find their answers. Write student answers on the board and have them copy the answers into their notebooks.

### Answers
1. All reptiles have lungs and scales or plates.
2. Birds use the long feathers on their wings and tails for flying. Birds' smaller body feathers help keep them warm.
3. Ostriches run very fast.

## Mammals, pages 86–87

### Preview Pages

Call students' attention to the heading, pictures, and captions before reading. Allow students to say whatever they can about the pictures and captions. Keep vocabulary explanations to a minimum for now.

### Teach Pages

Read the text and the captions aloud, or call on individual students to read them. Help students with new words. Elicit the key word (mammals), the sentence it is in, and the definition. Have students read the pages again to themselves. Alternatively, have students read aloud to each other in pairs or small groups.

**Understand Information** Ask picture and comprehension questions such as, *Where do most mammals live? Where do whales and dolphins live? Where do mammals with a lot of fur or hair live? Which picture shows a mammal with a lot of fur? Do mammals that live in warm places have much hair or fur? What are three mammals without much hair? Do mammals hatch from eggs?* Continue asking similar questions about all the pictures and the text.

**Organize Information** Have students make a word web of the mammal traits introduced on these pages. Draw the beginning of a web on the board and ask students to start one in their notebooks. Elicit one or two traits from the class and write them on the web. Have students work individually, in pairs, or in small groups to complete the webs in their notebooks. Check answers as a class. Have volunteers complete the web on the board.

---

### Leaders in Science: Jane Goodall

Point to the picture and ask students to talk about what they see in the photograph. Read the text and the caption aloud, or call on individual students to read them. Help students with new words. Have students read the selection again to themselves. Ask comprehension questions. Ask, *What other scientists do you know about?* (Dian Fossey, Joseph Priestley, George Washington Carver)

---

### Language Tip: *Young* (adjective) / *Young* (noun)

Remind students that some words can be a verb or a noun and look the same or similar. Use the example of *breathe* and *breath* or other words from page 68. Then tell students that some words can be both an adjective and a noun. Check that students understand the meaning of *adjective*. Give an example sentence to help them. Point to the Language Tip box on page 87 and ask a student to read the text. Have students find the sentences in the reading passage that contain the word *young*. Elicit which sentences show *young* as an adjective (All young mammals

*(continued)*

grow inside their mother's body. Most young mammals . . . ) and which sentences show *young* as a noun (Then the mother gives birth to live young. All mammal mothers feed milk to their young. When the young are old enough . . . ). Choose other examples of words from this unit that can be adjectives or nouns. (living things/the living, inside parts/the inside, outside parts/the outside) Have students work with a partner to make sentences using these words as adjectives and nouns.

---

**MUSIC CONNECTION: Whale Songs**

Read the text aloud or call on individual students to read it. Help students with new words. Ask if they see a key word in the text. (communicate) Have students read the text again to themselves. Ask comprehension questions.

---

### Before You Go On

Have pairs of students answer the first two questions. Have them write the questions and answers in their notebooks. Check answers before going on. Answer the third question together as a class.

**Possible Answers**
1. Mammals live on land and in water. Mammals live in cold places and warm places.
2. Fur and hair keep an animal warm.
3. Humans feed them, give them shelter, buy them clothes, take them places, play with them, teach them, and so on.

For more information, go to www.longmanusa.com/science for links to interesting websites about animals.

---

# Review and Practice, pages 88–89

## Vocabulary

If students need help reviewing the vocabulary, see the Optional Vocabulary Activities (pages vii–viii). Have students complete the exercise individually. Check answers as a class.

**Answers**

| | | |
|---|---|---|
| 1. communicate | 3. vertebrates | 5. reptiles |
| 2. invertebrates | 4. amphibians | 6. Mammals |

## Check Your Understanding

Have students answer the questions individually, in pairs, or in small groups. If students need extra support, tell them to look at the information in their notebooks or allow students to look back at the text. Then have students share their answers with the class. Write the answers on the board.

**Answers**
1. Birds have feathers and hatch from eggs.
2. Amphibians are born in the water and later live on land.
3. Fish have gills, scales, and live in water.
4. Reptiles have lungs and scales or plates.

## Apply Science Skills

**Science Reading Strategy: Key Sentences** Review the science reading strategy. Ask students, *What are key sentences? How do they help you understand?*

Read the instructions aloud, or call on a student to read them. Have students copy the diagram into their notebooks and complete it in pairs, in groups, or individually. Check answers by having volunteers complete the diagram on the board. Challenge students to find more key sentences. The completed diagram might look like this:

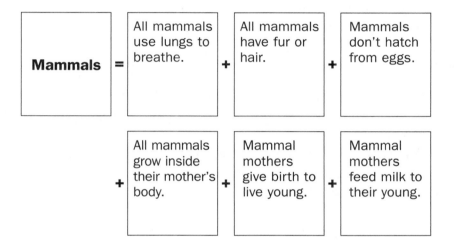

**Using Visuals: Pie Charts** Review what students learned about pie charts. Read the instructions aloud, or call on individual students to read them. Ask comprehension questions to review concepts.

Allow students to study the pie charts for a few minutes. Then have students ask and answer the questions in pairs. Check answers as a class. Discuss with students their reaction to this information.

**Answers**
1. Fish are the most endangered. 34% are endangered.
2. Birds are the least endangered. 11% are endangered.
3. Mammals and amphibians have the same percent of endangered species.

## Discuss

Encourage students to review the animals in the book, if needed, to make their choices. Then have students discuss the questions in pairs or small groups. Tell students to offer reasons for their opinions. Circulate to help and comment on students' choices. Allow time for students to share their opinions with the whole class.

Workbook pages 43–44 may now be assigned.

## Evaluation

### Self-Assessment Questions

Write the following questions on the board. Have students respond in their notebooks. Encourage students to share their responses in small groups or as a class.

1. How can I use key sentences to help me in reading?
2. How can pie charts help me understand information?
3. What was difficult for me in this lesson?
4. What was easy for me in this lesson?
5. What was most enjoyable in this lesson?

# Unit Review, pages 90–91

## Warm Up

Have pairs of students list the main ideas from Unit 2. Ask students to use the reading selection headings to group the main ideas. Alternatively, students may organize the main ideas in a word web.

Ask pairs to exchange their completed lists or word webs. Each pair should review the list or word web to see if any important information is missing. If information is missing, the pair should add it.

## Vocabulary

Have students work individually, with a partner, or in small groups, depending on how much support they need. Check answers as a class, writing the answers on the board.

---

**Answers**
1. A carnivore eats only other animals.
2. An herbivore eats only plants.
3. An omnivore eats both plants and animals.
4. An animal needs oxygen, water, food, and shelter to survive.
5. Animals with backbones are called vertebrates.
6. Animals without backbones are called invertebrates.
7. Turtles, lizards, and snakes are reptiles.
8. Amphibians have gills first and lungs later.
9. Mammals have fur or hair and give birth to live young.
10. We call the different kinds of animals in the animal kingdom *species*.
11. Animals communicate with their bodies and sounds.
12. Hair color, eye color, and tooth shape are examples of traits.

---

## Check Your Understanding

Have students work individually, with a partner, or in small groups, depending on how much support they need. Have students share their answers as a class. Write the correct answers on the board.

> **Answers**
> 1. False. There are more invertebrates than vertebrates.
> 2. False. Humans are vertebrate omnivores.
> 3. False. All birds have wings, but not all can fly.
> 4. True
> 6. False. Animals need oxygen, water, food, and shelter to survive.

## Extension Project

Have students do this project individually, in pairs, or in small groups. You may want to specify a certain number of sentences students should write (3–7 sentences).

Write on the board what each sentence of the paragraph should contain, for example:

1. What's the name of the animal you like?
2. What is the animal's body like? (trait).
3. What else is its body like? (trait).
4. Where does the animal live?
5. What is the animal's shelter?
6. Is it carnivore, herbivore, or omnivore?
7. What does the animal eat?

Have students copy this list into their notebooks before they begin writing their paragraphs.

## Apply Science Skills

**Using Visuals: Pie Charts** Read the instructions aloud, or call on a student to read them. Point to the box with the animal names. Have pairs of students read the names and then copy the incomplete chart into their notebooks. Ask students to write *vertebrate* or *invertebrate* next to the correct percentage. Check answers. Have students work individually, in pairs, or in small groups to complete their pie charts. Check answers as a class.

> **Answers**
> Invertebrates: jellyfish, spiders, crabs, butterflies, sponges
> Vertebrates: fish, humans, frogs, lions, birds

## Read More About It

Bring at least one of the suggested books to class. Show the cover and some of the inside pages to students as a preview. Ask students to predict what the book is about.

Read an excerpt aloud to the class. Then ask several comprehension questions. Read the excerpt again before calling on students to answer. Encourage students to find this or another suggested book in their school library or local bookstore.

Workbook pages 45–46 may now be assigned.

## Unit Experiment, pages 92–93
### What Traits Do Animals Share?

**Note:** For this experiment, you can collect examples of the animals listed on the page from a garden and local pet store (ant, cricket, snail, goldfish). Alternatively, you can bring in other small animals or photographs of animals and objects. Make sure containers with animals and objects are labeled.

### Preview

Begin this section with books closed. Elicit and review the five steps of the scientific method. Have students look at the photo of Jane Goodall on page 86. Ask, *What is Goodall doing?* (observing) Tell students, *Observing is a good way to learn about animals.*

Call on a student to read the experiment title aloud. Tell students, *This is our main question.* Read aloud the introduction, purpose, and materials, or have individual students read them.

On the board, write *Observe. Write down observations. Draw conclusions.* Tell students, *We'll observe animals. We'll find out about their traits. We'll write down our observations. Then we'll draw conclusions.*

### Do the Experiment

Read the What to Do instructions aloud, or have a student read them. Point out the data table. Tell students that the data table is also on Workbook page 47. Show the animals they will study and list the names on the board. Model observing and writing information about the first animal or object. Have students copy the information into their Workbook data charts.

Have pairs or small groups of students observe the animals. Have them complete the Experiment Log after observing each animal or item. When the experiment has been completed, elicit conclusions and have students add the information to their logs.

Workbook page 47 should be used to record the steps during the experiment. Then Workbook page 48 can be assigned.

# Unit 3 Rocks and Minerals

## Unit Overview

| Lesson | Content | Science Skills | | Experiment |
| | | Reading Strategies | Using Visuals | |
|---|---|---|---|---|
| 1 | • What Are Rocks and Minerals? Igneous Rock, Sedimentary Rock, Metamorphic Rock | Ask Questions | Sectional Diagrams | How Do Rocks Change? |
| 2 | • The Earth's Changing Surface: Weathering, Erosion, Earthquakes, Volcanoes | Cause and Effect | Photo Sequences | |

## Objectives

**Vocabulary**
• Develop new vocabulary related to rocks and minerals
• Use newly acquired vocabulary in context

**Concepts**
• Learn about igneous, sedimentary, and metamorphic rock
• Learn about erosion and weathering of rock
• Learn about volcanoes, earthquakes, and tsunami

**Reading Strategies**
• Ask questions to understand and remember information
• Understand cause and effect in a text to improve comprehension
• Practice previously learned strategies

**Using Visuals**
• Understand how to study sectional diagrams for information
• Understand how to study photo sequences for information

**Experiment**
• Understand the rock cycle

# Unit Opener, pages 94–95

## Preview Topic

Ask students to preview these pages. Then ask, *What is this unit about? What do you already know about rocks and minerals? What do you think you'll learn in this unit?* Ask students what they see in the pictures. Encourage them to say whatever they can. Point to each picture and give a little more information about it.

### Unit Concepts

Read aloud the list of unit concepts for Lessons 1 and 2. Ask, *What words and sentences do you understand?* Elicit information about them. Tell students they'll learn the other information as they read the lessons.

### Get Ready

Point to the Get Ready box. Read the instructions aloud, or call on individual students to read them. Help students understand and pronounce new words. Let students reread silently if helpful. Ask comprehension questions such as, *How many rocks will you need? Do the rocks need to be different?*

Have students collect rocks as a class, or assign the collecting for homework in advance, or bring an assortment of rocks to the classroom. Have students copy the chart into their notebooks. Hold up a rock. Say, *What color is this? It's brown and gray. I'll write that in the chart. What shape is it?*

Have students complete their charts individually, in pairs, or small groups. Circulate to help and encourage students. When they have finished, call on several students to show and tell about their most interesting rock.

# Lesson ❶

# Before You Read, pages 96–99

Have students preview these pages individually or in pairs. Ask, *What will you learn in this lesson?*

## Vocabulary

Read the captions aloud, or call on students to read them. Help students understand and pronounce new words. Use pictures, props, and mime. Have students read the captions again silently. Ask picture and comprehension questions for each item. Read the key words (page 97) aloud and have students say them after you. Then have students close their books. Point to the pictures and ask questions to elicit the key words.

### Practice

Have students write the sentences in their notebooks, leaving a space for each answer. Then have them choose the correct answers and write them in the sentences.

Check answers by calling on individual students. Write the letters of the correct answers on the board.

**Answers**
1. a. properties
2. b. volcano
3. c. mineral
4. c. Sedimentary
5. b. igneous
6. a. Metamorphic

Workbook page 49 may now be assigned.

## Science Skills

**Science Reading Strategy: Ask Questions** With books closed, ask students, *In class, what do I ask you after you read?* (questions) *Why do I ask questions?* (to make sure we understand, to help us remember) Say, *When you read, ask yourself questions. This will help you understand the text. It will also help you remember it.* Ask, *What are some question words beginning with* Wh-? *What's a question word beginning with* H-? *What are some* yes-no *question words?* Elicit and write question words on the board. (*What, Where, When, Why, Which, How, Is/Are, Do/Does*)

Have students open their books to page 98. Read the heading, introduction, and instructions aloud, or call on individual students to read them. Tell students to reread the instructions silently. Then ask, *What are you going to do after you read each sentence?*

Preteach new words. Have students read the paragraph and ask and answer the questions silently as they read. Next, have students ask and answer the questions in pairs. Then call on individual students to answer the questions.

Tell students, *Ask yourself questions as you read. This will help you understand the reading. It will also help you remember the information.*

**Answers**
1. The Big Island of Hawaii has black sand beaches.
2. The sand is black because it is made of dark igneous rock.
3. A volcano erupted many years ago.
4. Hot liquid rock poured out of the volcano.
5. The sand was made when hot liquid rock hit the cold ocean water and exploded into tiny pieces.

Workbook pages 50–51 may now be assigned.

**Using Visuals: Sectional Diagrams** Hold up your book and point to the diagram of the earth. Say, *This is a sectional diagram. Sectional diagrams have one or more pieces cut away. You can see inside something. What does this sectional diagram show the inside of? How many layers does this diagram show?* Say, *Sectional diagrams give us information about the inside of things.*

Have students read the heading at the top of the page. Read the introduction, caption, and questions aloud, or call on individual students to read them. Have students reread silently. Ask questions to check understanding and elicit meanings of vocabulary. Have students study the diagram and color key for a few minutes.

Then assign pairs to ask and answer the questions. Have students write their answers in their notebooks. Check by eliciting correct answers and writing them on the board.

> **Answers**
> 1. The hottest layer of the earth is made of solid metal.
> 2. The coolest layer of the earth is made of solid rock.
> 3. The soft rock and liquid metal layers are not solid.

 Workbook page 52 may now be assigned.

## Lesson ❶

## What Are Rocks and Minerals? pages 100–101

### Preview Pages

Have students preview the pages and predict the topic. Ask, *What are you going to learn on these pages? What do you already know about rocks and minerals?*

### Teach Pages

Read the text and the captions aloud, or call on individual students to read them. Help students with new words. Elicit the key word (mineral), the sentence it is in, and the definition. Have students read the pages again to themselves. Alternatively, have pairs or small groups of students read aloud to each other. Remind students to use the reading strategies they have learned in other units to help them understand. In pairs, have students ask each other questions about the reading. Follow up with your own comprehension and picture questions.

**Understand Information** Read the first sentence aloud again. Say, *We practiced asking questions with the black sand reading on page 98. Let's practice that reading strategy here. What are some question words we can use?* (What, Who, Where, When, How, Why) Write them on the board. *What question can we ask for the first sentence?* (What covers the earth's surface? / What do rocks cover?) Read the second sentence, elicit a question, and write it on the board. Continue with each sentence on these pages.

Tell students, *Now read the pages again silently. Ask yourself questions as you read.* Encourage emergent readers to look at the board when they need help with a question. When students have finished, have pairs or small groups of students take turns asking and answering questions.

**Organize Information** Have students make a Main Idea and Details chart for the first paragraph on page 101. If needed, elicit the main idea or one of the details. The chart might look like this:

| Main Idea |
| :---: |
| All rocks are made of minerals. |

| Detail | Detail |
| :--- | :--- |
| Usually rocks are made of several minerals. | But sometimes they are made of only one or two. |

## REACHING ALL STUDENTS: Visual and Kinesthetic Learners

Bring some table salt to class. Place a small amount, so that individual grains are visible, in one or more dishes. Have students look at it with a hand lens. Have students draw a picture of a salt crystal in their notebooks and label it *halite*. Elicit the three traits of a mineral. (It is solid. It has crystals. It comes from nature.) Write the traits on the board and have students copy them into their notebooks.

## Language Tip: Word Families: *Nature*

Have students read the text in the Language Tip box. Write *nature* ⟶ *noun*, *natural* ⟶ *adjective*, *naturally* ⟶ *adverb* on the board and have students copy this in their notebooks. Next to each line, write an example sentence for students to copy, such as, *A rock comes from* <u>nature</u>. *It is a* <u>natural</u> *thing. It is made* <u>naturally</u>. Remind students, *Adjectives tell more about a noun. Adverbs tell more about a verb. What noun does* natural *tell about?* (thing) *What verb does* naturally *tell about?* (made) Circle *thing* and *made* on the board. Say, *Find a sentence on page 101 with the noun* nature *and the adverb* naturally. (A mineral must also come from nature, or happen naturally.) Have students copy this sentence into their notebooks as you write it on the board. Ask students to underline the noun *nature* and the adverb *naturally*, then circle the verb that *naturally* tells about.

### Before You Go On

Have pairs of students answer the first two questions. Have them write the questions and answers in their notebooks. Check answers before going on. Answer the third question together as a class.

**Answers**
1. Possible answers: You can find rocks at beaches and in streams. You can find them under water, ice, or soil. You can find them on mountains.
2. All minerals must be solid, or hard. They must have crystals. A mineral must come from nature.
3. No, because a mineral must come from nature.

# What Are Rocks and Minerals? (continued), pages 102–104

pages 102–104

## Preview Pages

Have students preview the pages and predict what they will learn. Point to the pictures of copper wire and a diamond and say, *Let's use what we know to compare and contrast copper and diamonds.* Remind students that when they compare and contrast, they think about how things are the same and different. State a similarity by saying, *Copper and diamonds are both minerals.* Ask, *How are copper and diamonds different?*

## Teach Pages

Read the text and the captions aloud, or call on individual students to read them. Help students with new words. Elicit any key words (mineral, properties), the sentences they are in, and their definitions. Have students read the pages again to themselves. Remind students to use the reading strategies they have learned in other units to help them understand. In pairs, have students ask each other questions about the reading. Follow up with your own comprehension and picture questions.

**Understand Information** Say, *Let's practice asking questions as we read the first paragraph again. What are some questions we can ask for this first paragraph?* Elicit two or three questions about the paragraph and write them on the board. Tell students, *Now read the pages again silently. Ask yourself questions as you read.* When students have finished, have students take turns asking and answering questions in pairs or small groups.

Have students look at the diagram. Ask, *What kind of diagram is this?* (sectional diagram) Have students look back at page 99, if needed. Ask, *What does a sectional diagram show?* (the inside of something) *What does this sectional diagram show? What are the four layers? What layer is the surface of the earth? What layer is made of hot, soft rock? What layer is made of liquid metal? What layer is made of solid metal?*

**Organize Information** Have students make a Main Idea and Details chart about the information on page 103. Encourage students to add as much detail as possible to their charts. The chart might look like this:

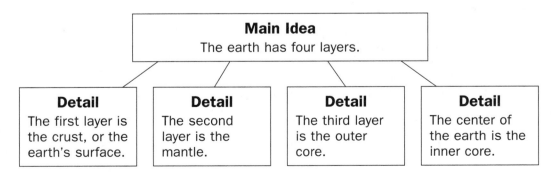

**Main Idea**
The earth has four layers.

**Detail**
The first layer is the crust, or the earth's surface.

**Detail**
The second layer is the mantle.

**Detail**
The third layer is the outer core.

**Detail**
The center of the earth is the inner core.

## Language Tip: Plural Form: -y ⟶ -ies

Have students read the text in the Language Tip box. Write *property* ⟶ *properties* on the board and have students write it in their notebooks. Ask, *What letter does* property *end with?* (-*y*) Say, *To make the plural form, we usually change the* y *to* i *and add* -es. Ask, *What are some other nouns ending in* -y? (party, city, baby, lady, country) Write these words or students' suggestions on the board. Have students copy them into their notebooks and then write the plural forms. Call on students to spell out the plural forms, or write them on the board. Encourage students to create example sentences using the plural forms.

## HEALTH CONNECTION: Minerals We Eat

Ask students to look at the title and picture to predict what the text might be about. Read the text aloud, or call on a student to read it. Help students with new words. Ask comprehension questions.

Make copies of the nutrition facts on a food product, such as cereal, and pass them out to the class. Explain how to read a nutrition facts label. Have students find calcium and what percent the food supplies. Write names of other minerals on the board. (sodium [salt], copper, iron, potassium, phosphorus, magnesium, zinc) In pairs or groups, have students find these minerals on the label. Discuss how much of the mineral the food supplies and how much people need every day.

## Science Now: Using the Earth's Heat

Ask students to look at the title and picture to predict what the text might be about. Read the text aloud, or call on a student to read it. Help students with new words. Ask comprehension questions.

Say, *Sometimes underground hot water comes to the surface of the earth. We can see that at Yellowstone National Park.* Have students look at pictures of Yellowstone's hot springs, vents, and geysers on the Internet.

## Before You Go On

Have pairs of students answer the first two questions. Have them write the questions and answers in their notebooks. Check answers before going on. Answer the third question together as a class.

### Answers
1. Two properties of copper are that it can carry electricity and it can be shaped easily.
2. The four layers of the earth are the crust, the mantle, the outer core, and the inner core.
3. The hot liquid from a volcano comes from the mantle because that layer is hot soft rock.

## Igneous Rock, page 104
## Sedimentary Rock, page 105

### Preview Pages

Have students preview the pages and predict what they will learn.

Point to the picture of the cooling igneous rock and the sedimentary rock on the opposite page and say, *Let's use what we know to compare and contrast the pictures of these two types of rocks.* Ask, *What is the same about these rocks? How are they different?*

### Teach Pages

Read the text and the captions aloud, or call on individual students to read them. Help students with new words. Elicit any key words (igneous, sedimentary), the sentences they are in, and their definitions. Have students read the pages again to themselves. Alternatively, have pairs or small groups of students read aloud to each other. Remind students to use the reading strategies they have learned in other units to help them understand. Have students ask each other questions about the reading in pairs. Follow up with your own comprehension and picture questions.

**Understand Information** Say, *Let's practice asking questions as we read the first paragraph again. What are some questions we can ask for this paragraph?* If students can form questions without your help, elicit questions for the first paragraph only, then continue on to the rereading of the pages. Otherwise, elicit two or three questions about each paragraph and write them on the board.

Tell students, *Now read the pages again silently. Ask yourself questions as you read.* When students have finished, have pairs or small groups of students take turns asking and answering questions. Check that students are using the strategy by asking the most important questions to elicit key information.

### As You Read: Ask Questions

Read the information aloud or call on a student to read it. Ask students what questions they asked themselves as they read the information about sedimentary rock. List the questions on the board. Have pairs or small groups ask and answer the questions.

**Organize Information** Have students make a chart listing important information about igneous rock, both extrusive and intrusive, and sedimentary rock. Say (and write on the board), *Find one key sentence about extrusive rock, one key sentence about intrusive igneous rock, and four key sentences about sedimentary rock. Write the sentences in your chart.* The chart might look like this:

| Igneous Rock | | Sedimentary Rock |
|---|---|---|
| Igneous rock forms when hot liquid rock cools and becomes hard. | | Sand, mud, and tiny pieces of rock form layers over time. These layers sit on top of one another. The heavy weight of the top layers causes the bottom layers to join together. These layers become sedimentary rock. |
| **Extrusive** | **Intrusive** | |
| The liquid rock cools and hardens above ground. | The liquid rock cools and hardens underground. | |

## Science at Home: Pumice

Ask students to look at the title and photograph to predict what the text might be about. Bring in a pumice stone and allow students to see and touch it. Demonstrate how it is used for rough areas of the skin. Read the text aloud, or call on a student to read it. Help students with new words. Ask comprehension questions.

## Before You Go On

Have pairs of students answer the first two questions. Have them write the questions and answers in their notebooks. Check answers before going on. Answer the third question together as a class.

### Answers
1. Two types of igneous rock are extrusive igneous rock and intrusive igneous rock.
2. Sand, mud, and tiny pieces of rock can form layers of sedimentary rock.
3. No, because sedimentary rock is made of sand and pieces of other rocks. First there was igneous rock. Later, this rock became sedimentary rock.

## Metamorphic Rock, page 106

### Preview Page

Have students preview the page and predict what they will learn.

### Teach Page

Read the text and the captions aloud, or call on individual students to read them. Help students with new words. Elicit any key words (metamorphic, igneous, sedimentary), the sentences they are in, and their definitions. Have students read the pages again to themselves. Alternatively, have students read aloud to each other in pairs or small groups. Remind students to use the reading strategies they have learned in other units to help them understand. Have pairs of students ask each other questions about the reading. Follow up with your own comprehension and picture questions.

**Understand Information** Say, *Ask questions as you reread this page.* Elicit and help students with a question for the first sentence. (Where is there heat and pressure?) Say, *I'll ask about your questions after you read.* When students have finished, have pairs or small groups of students take turns asking and answering their questions. Then elicit questions from students and write them on the board.

**Organize Information** Have students make a chart about metamorphic rock using information on this page. Tell students, *Find three key sentences for how metamorphic rock is made, what it looks like, and examples.* The chart might look like this:

| Metamorphic Rock |
| --- |
| Heat and pressure can change igneous rock and sedimentary rock to metamorphic rock. |
| It usually has layers that fold over each other. |
| Marble and slate are metamorphic rocks. |

## Optional Activity

Bring in samples of igneous rock, sedimentary rock, and metamorphic rock. Let students touch them and look at them closely with a hand lens. Draw a chart on the board, similar to that on page 94, labeled *igneous rock, sedimentary rock, metamorphic rock* on the left and *color, shape, texture* at the top. In pairs or groups, have students discuss and write down their observations. Check by eliciting information and writing it on the board.

# Exploring, page 107

### Preview Page

Have students preview the page and predict what they will learn.

### Teach Page

Read the text and captions aloud, or call on individual students to read them. Help students with new words. Elicit any key words (igneous, sedimentary, metamorphic, volcano), the sentences they are in, and their definitions. Have students read the page again to themselves. Alternatively, have pairs or small groups of students read aloud to each other. Remind students to use the reading strategies they have learned in other units to help them understand.

**Understand Information** Ask, *What reading strategy are we practicing in this lesson?* Say, *Ask questions as you reread page 107. I'll ask about your questions after you read.* This time have students work individually on their questions, and check them as a class.

Ask critical-thinking questions about the rock cycle diagram or put them on the board and have students discuss them in pairs or small groups. For example, ask, *What makes igneous rock?* (liquid rock, volcanic activity) *How can igneous rock change into sedimentary rock?* (It breaks down into sand. Then layers of mud, sand, and rock become sedimentary rock.) *How can igneous rock become metamorphic rock?* (It is melted or squeezed deep underground.) *How can igneous rock become liquid rock?* (Hot liquid rock can melt it.) *How can metamorphic rock become sedimentary rock?* (It breaks down into sand. Then layers of mud, sand, and rock become sedimentary rock.)

**Organize Information** The information on this page is organized into a cycle diagram. Review cycle diagrams with students, referring to Unit 1, if needed. You may want students to copy the rock cycle into their notebooks.

## Before You Go On

Have pairs of students answer the first two questions. Have them write the questions and answers in their notebooks. Check answers before going on. Answer the third question together as a class.

**Answers**
1. Metamorphic rock forms deep underground.
2. Marble and slate are two types of metamorphic rock.
3. Possible answer: Rock is good for making buildings because it is hard, strong, and long lasting.

For more information, go to www.longmanusa.com/science for links to interesting websites about rocks and minerals.

# Review and Practice, pages 108–109

## Vocabulary

If students need help in reviewing this vocabulary, see the Optional Vocabulary Activities (pages vii–viii). Have students complete the exercise individually.

**Answers**
1. igneous
2. sedimentary
3. metamorphic
4. volcano
5. mineral
6. properties

## Check Your Understanding

Have students answer the questions individually, in pairs, or in small groups. If students need extra support, tell them to look at the information in their notebooks or allow students to look back at the text. Then have students share their answers with the class. Write the answers on the board.

**Answers**
1. All rocks are made of minerals.
2. The four layers of the earth are the crust, the mantle, the outer core, and the inner core.
3. Metamorphic rock is formed when igneous or sedimentary rock is changed by heat and pressure underground.
4. The rock cycle shows that rocks can change.

## Apply Science Skills

**Science Reading Strategy: Ask Questions** Read the instructions aloud, or call on a student to read the instructions. Have students look back at the reading on pages 102–103. Elicit one question and write it on the board, if helpful. Then, individually or in pairs, have students make questions for the text. Check students' questions as a class.

**Using Visuals: Sectional Diagrams** Tell students, *You used sectional diagrams to learn about the inside of the earth. This sectional diagram will show you some new information.* Read the instructions and questions aloud, or call on individual students to read them. Have students reread silently, if helpful. Tell students that to answer the third question they need to use what they know.

Have students study the diagram for a few minutes. Then have pairs of students ask and answer the questions. Have them write their answers in their notebooks. Then elicit answers and write them on the board.

> **Answers**
> 1. Extrusive igneous rock hardens above the ground.
> 2. Intrusive igneous rock hardens below the ground.
> 3. The hot liquid rock comes from the mantle deep underground.

## Discuss

Read the discussion questions aloud. Have students discuss the questions in pairs, in small groups, or as a class. You may want students to make a bulletin board display of things made from rock. Invite students to bring in pictures and to identify what type of rock was used.

Workbook pages 53–54 may now be assigned.

## Evaluation

### Self-Assessment Questions

Write the following questions on the board and have students respond in their notebooks. Encourage students to share their responses in small groups or as a class.

1. How can asking questions help me in reading?
2. How can sectional diagrams help me understand new ideas?
3. What was difficult for me in this lesson?
4. What was easy for me in this lesson?
5. What was most enjoyable in this lesson?

# Lesson ❷

## Before You Read, pages 110–113

Have students preview these pages individually or in pairs. Ask, *What will you learn in this lesson?*

### Vocabulary

Read the captions aloud, or call on students to read them. Help students understand and pronounce new words. Use pictures, props, and mime. Have students read the captions again silently. Ask picture and comprehension questions for each item. Read the key words (page 111) aloud and have students say them after you. Then have students close their books. Point to the pictures and ask questions to elicit the key words.

### Practice

Read the instructions aloud. Elicit one or more definitions, if helpful. Have students define the words in pairs or small groups. Check by calling on individual students to read their sentences. Write the definitions on the board.

> **Possible Answers**
> · earthquake: the ground shakes
> · erosion: wind and water move pieces of rock away
> · glacier: a big sheet of ice on a mountain
> · geologist: a scientist who studies rocks
> · geology: the study of rocks
> · weathering: wind and water break off pieces of rock

 Workbook page 55 may now be assigned.

### Science Skills

 **Science Reading Strategy: Cause and Effect** To demonstrate cause and effect, push some papers around your desk until you knock them on the floor. Ask, *Why are these papers on the floor? What happened?* Elicit from students that you caused the papers to fall on the floor. Write *Cause* on the board and draw a circle under it. In the circle write, *I knocked the papers off the desk.* Draw an arrow pointing to another circle labeled *Effect*. Say, *I knocked the papers off my desk. What happened to the papers? What was the effect?* Elicit that the papers fell on the floor. Write that sentence in the circle labeled *Effect*. Say, *Many things have a cause, and as a result, there are effects.*

Have students open their books to page 112. Ask students to cover the diagram with their notebooks. Read the heading and introduction aloud or call on individual students to read them. Have students reread them silently, if helpful. Ask, *What does a cause do? What is the effect? What words often tell about cause and effect?*

Read or call on individual students to read the text aloud. Help students with new words. Have students look at the picture. Ask, *What happened to the building? What happened to the car? What's the cause? What are the effects?* Remind students to look for cause and effect as they read this lesson.

Workbook pages 56–57 may now be assigned.

**Using Visuals: Photo Sequences** Have students look at the Mount St. Helens photo sequence on page 121. Hold up your book and point to the pictures. Say, *This is a volcano. What do these pictures show? What does the first picture show? What does the second picture show? What does the last picture show?* Say, *These photos show an event in three photos. They show what happened before, during, and after the event. We call this visual a photo sequence. Photo sequences can give us a lot of information.*

Have students read the heading at the top of page 113. Ask students, *What visuals did you learn about in other lessons?* (diagrams, cycle diagrams, photographs, pie charts, sectional diagrams) Ask, *What visual will you practice using in this lesson?*

Read the introduction and the captions aloud, or call on individual students to read them. Help students with new words. Have students reread silently. Ask questions to check comprehension. Have students study the photos for a few minutes. Then have pairs ask and answer the questions. Have them write their answers in their notebooks. Check answers and write them on the board.

---

**Possible Answers**
1. Before the tsunami, the land is green. There is much vegetation. There are buildings.
2. After the tsunami, the land looks empty. The trees and buildings are gone.
3. The tsunami took away some of the beach and destroyed the trees.

---

Workbook page 58 may now be assigned.

# Lesson ❷

## The Earth's Changing Surface, pages 114–121
## Weathering, pages 114–115

### Preview Pages

Have students preview the pages and predict what they will learn.

### Teach Pages

Read the text and the captions aloud, or call on individual students to read them. Help students with new words. Elicit the key word (weathering), the sentence it is in, and the definition. Have students read the pages again to themselves. Alternatively, have pairs or small groups of students read aloud to each other.

**Understand Information** Ask picture and comprehension questions such as, *What is one way rocks change? What is weathering? How long does weathering take? Can weathering take a few years? What causes weathering? Can water break rock when it freezes? What does the salt in seawater do?* Continue asking similar questions about all the pictures and the text.

**Organize Information** Tell students, *Now you'll make a Cause-and-Effect diagram showing what causes weathering.* Draw a Cause-and-Effect diagram labeled *Weathering.* Write, *Weathering breaks down rocks* in the *Effect* circle. Tell students, *Find all the things that cause a rock to weather.* Hold up your book and point to both text and captions. Say, *Look at both the text and the captions.* The diagram might look like this:

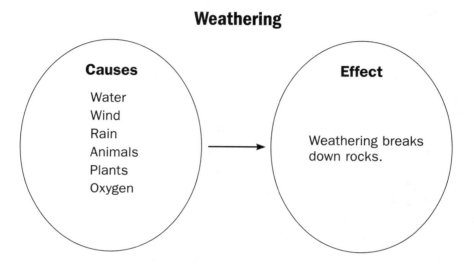

**Weathering**

Causes

Water
Wind
Rain
Animals
Plants
Oxygen

Effect

Weathering breaks down rocks.

---

**Language Tip:** *Weathering*

Have students read the text in the Language Tip box. Write *weathering* on the board and underline *-ing*. Ask, *What kinds of words end in* -ing? (verbs) Explain that sometimes we use a word that ends in *-ing* as a noun instead of a verb. Give example sentences of *weathering* as a noun and as a verb. (Weathering is a very slow process. [noun] The wind is weathering this statue. [verb])

---

**Before You Go On**

Have pairs of students answer the first two questions. Have them write the questions and answers in their notebooks. Check answers before going on. Answer the third question together as a class.

**Answers**
1. Weathering breaks rock into small pieces or weakens it.
2. Water can break off pieces of rock when it freezes. Saltwater and rain weaken rock.
3. Yes, because after rocks break into smaller pieces they can form sand.

## Erosion, pages 116–117

### Preview Pages

Have students preview and predict what they will learn.

Have students compare and contrast the pictures of the glacier and the wind in pairs. When students have finished, elicit similarities and differences.

### Teach Pages

Read the text and the captions aloud, or call on individual students to read them. Help students with new words. Elicit any key words (erosion, weathering), the sentences they are in, and their definitions. Have students read the pages again to themselves. Alternatively, have pairs or small groups of students read aloud to each other.

**Understand Information** Ask picture and comprehension questions such as, *What do wind, water, and ice do? What is erosion? Can wind carry sand? Can glaciers carry rocks? How? What makes the land look different? Where does the wind take the sand? How does the rock's shape change?* Continue asking similar questions about all the pictures and the text.

**Organize Information** Tell students, *Now you'll make a Cause-and-Effect diagram showing the causes of erosion.* Draw a diagram labeled *Erosion,* and write *Erosion moves loose pieces of rock and soil* in the *Effect* circle. Make another circle labeled *Causes.* Tell students, *Find all the things that cause erosion.* Hold up your book and point to both text and captions. Say, *Look at both the text and the captions.* Check answers and write student responses on the board. The diagram might look like this:

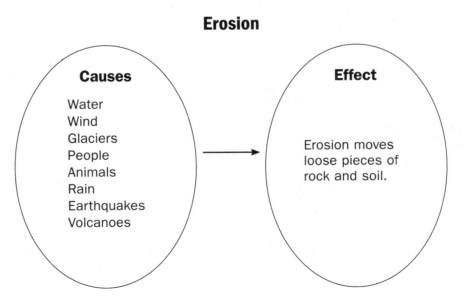

**Erosion**

**Causes**

Water
Wind
Glaciers
People
Animals
Rain
Earthquakes
Volcanoes

**Effect**

Erosion moves
loose pieces of
rock and soil.

## Science at Home: Rounded Rocks

Ask students to look at the title and photograph to predict what the text might be about. Bring in a rounded, smooth rock for students to see and touch. Read the text aloud, or call on a student to read it. Help students with new words. Ask comprehension questions.

Have students find a rounded rock and bring it to the next class. Have students share their rocks with others. Ask individual students, *Where did you find your rock? Was it near a river? How was it weathered? How long do you think it took to weather the rock?*

## Environment Watch: Soil Erosion

Ask students to look at the title and photo to predict what the text might be about. Have students look at the picture. Ask, *What happened in this picture?* (Trees and mud fell off a hill.) *What happened to the buildings?* (The trees and mud fell on them.) *What caused this?* (Possible answer: Maybe rain caused this.) Read the text aloud, or call on a student to read it. Help students with new words. Ask comprehension questions.

## Optional Activity

Have students find examples of erosion in their community. Take students on a walk near the school (if you can locate erosion beforehand) or to a park on a field trip. Alternatively, assign this activity for homework. Have students take or draw pictures of the erosion. Have them write sentences about where the erosion took place and what they think caused it.

### Before You Go On

Have pairs of students answer the first two questions. Have them write the questions and answers in their notebooks. Check answers before going on. Answer the third question together as a class.

**Answers**
1. Possible answers: Examples of erosion: wind causing sand to build up in a new place, waves crashing against rock, soil washing down a hill.
2. Erosion is moving and reshaping of rock. Weathering is rock breaking into smaller pieces.
3. Weathering and erosion can change the shape of rock by wearing it away and making holes in it.

## Earthquakes, pages 118–119

## Preview Pages

Have students preview the pages and predict what they will learn.

## Teach Pages

Read the text and the captions aloud, or call on individual students to read them. Help students with new words. Elicit the key word (earthquake), the sentences it is in, and the definition. Have students read the pages again to themselves. Alternatively, have pairs or small groups of students read aloud to each other.

---

**Language Tip:** *Tsunami*

Have students read the text in the Language Tip box. Ask, *Where did you see the word* tsunami *before?* (Using Visuals, page 113) Explain that some words have the same form in singular and plural. Elicit or give other examples. (sheep, deer)

---

**Understand Information**  Ask picture and comprehension questions such as, *Does pressure build up under the earth's crust? What does this cause? Why does the ground shake? What is that called? What are faults? Are all earthquakes strong? Do they last a long time? What kind of damage do earthquakes cause?* Continue asking similar questions about all the pictures and the text.

---

**As You Read:** Cause and Effect

Read the As You Read text aloud, or call on a student to read it. Draw a Cause-and-Effect diagram on the board and have students make one in their notebooks. Label the diagram *Earthquakes*. Have students read page 118 again. Ask them to write a cause and at least one effect of an earthquake. Check answers as a class.

---

**Organize Information**  Have students make a sequence diagram using the information on page 119. The diagram might look like this:

### Tsunami

| Very strong earthquakes under the ocean can cause big waves. | → | When a tsunami reaches land, it can be very dangerous. It can cover everything in water. | → | It can kill people, animals, and plants. A tsunami can cause a lot of damage. |
|---|---|---|---|---|

## REACHING ALL STUDENTS: Visual Learners

Bring in a video or CD of earthquakes or tsunami. Alternatively, download or help students find moving and still images on the Internet. Discuss these images of earthquakes and tsunami with students to elicit and reinforce lesson concepts and vocabulary. Some students may have personal experiences to share about earthquakes or tsunami.

Have pairs of students answer the first two questions. Have them write the questions and answers in their notebooks. Check answers before going on. Answer the third question together as a class.

**Answers**

1. Earthquakes often happen where there are faults.
2. A very strong earthquake under the ocean can cause a tsunami.
3. Possible answer: Earthquakes and tsunami can remove or reshape beaches, cities, hills, and so forth.

## Volcanoes, pages 120–121

### Preview Pages

Have students preview the pages and predict what they will learn.

### Teach Pages

Read the text and the captions aloud, or call on individual students to read them. Help students with new words. There are no key words on these pages. Have students read the pages again to themselves. Alternatively, have students read aloud to each other in pairs or small groups.

**Understand Information** Ask picture and comprehension questions such as, *What is a volcano? Where does pressure build up? What happens when pressure builds up? Can a volcano explode violently? What comes out of a volcano? Does the liquid rock get hard or remain soft?* Continue asking similar questions about all the pictures and the text. Also, ask questions about cause and effect. *What causes a volcano to explode? What are the effects of a volcano erupting?*

**Organize Information** Focus students' attention on the photo sequence of Mount St. Helens. Ask, *What does this photo sequence show?* Tell students, *Let's make a sequence diagram of what happens when a volcano erupts.* Have students reread page 120. Draw a box on the board and write inside *Pressure builds up inside a volcano.* Have pairs of students complete the sequence diagram in their notebooks. When students have finished, ask volunteers to complete the diagram on the board. The diagram might look like this:

## A Volcanic Eruption

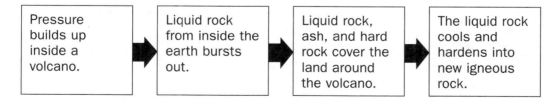

| Pressure builds up inside a volcano. | → | Liquid rock from inside the earth bursts out. | → | Liquid rock, ash, and hard rock cover the land around the volcano. | → | The liquid rock cools and hardens into new igneous rock. |

## Language Tip: *Hard/Harden*

Have students read the text in the Language Tip box. Tell students that similar words can be different parts of speech. Remind them about *breathe/breath* in Unit 2. Write *hard* and *harden* on the board. Say, Hard *is the adjective in this word family. Show me a sentence with* hard *on page 120.* Write the sentence on the board. Harden *is the verb in this word family. Show me a sentence with* harden *on page 120.* Write the sentence on the board. You may want to compare *hard/harden* with *soft/soften* because they function the same way.

## Leaders in Science: Sir Charles Lyell

Read the title, then point to the picture and ask students, *Who is this man? What kind of scientist was he? When did he live?* Read the text and captions aloud. Have students read the selection again silently. Ask comprehension questions.

## HISTORY CONNECTION: A City Is Destroyed

Ask students to look at the title and photo to predict what the text might be about. Read the text aloud, or call on a student to read it. Help students with new words. Ask comprehension questions. Drawing pictures on the board, explain that the bodies of the people left holes in the cold rock. Scientists plaster inside the holes. This makes models of the people who were there when the volcano erupted. Have students look at pictures of casts from Pompeii on the Internet.

### Before You Go On

Have pairs of students answer the first two questions. Have them write the questions and answers in their notebooks. Check answers before going on. Answer the third question together as a class.

**Answers**
1. Pressure builds up inside a volcano and causes it to erupt.
2. Mount St. Helens is an active volcano.
3. When a volcano erupts many times, there is a lot of new igneous rock around it. The new rock makes a mountain.

For more information, go to www.longmanusa.com/science for links to interesting websites about rocks and minerals.

# Review and Practice, pages 122–123

## Vocabulary

If students need help in reviewing the vocabulary, see the Optional Vocabulary Activities (pages vii–viii). Have students complete the exercise individually. Check answers as a class.

**Answers**

**1.** glacier      **3.** earthquake      **5.** erosion

**2.** geologist      **4.** weathering      **6.** Geology

## Check Your Understanding

Have students answer the questions individually, in pairs, or in small groups. If students need extra support, tell them to look at the information in their notebooks, or allow students to look back at the text. Then have students share their answers with the class. Write the answers on the board.

**Answers**

**1.** Plants, animals, wind, and water can cause weathering.

**2.** Glaciers, wind, and water can cause erosion.

**3.** When pressure builds under the earth's crust, it causes an earthquake.

**4.** New igneous rock is usually around a volcano because the hot molten rock from the volcano cools and hardens.

## Apply Science Skills

**Science Reading Strategy: Cause and Effect** Review the science reading strategy. Ask students, *What's an effect? What makes it happen?* Read the instructions aloud, or call on a student to read them. Have students copy the diagram into their notebooks as you write it on the board. Tell students to read the first two sentences on page 119 again and find the effect. Have students complete their diagrams in pairs or in small groups. When students are finished, elicit the effect (A big wave called a tsunami may result.) and write it on the board.

**Using Visuals: Photo Sequences** Tell students, *Photo sequences are one way scientists share information. You learned about photo sequences in this lesson. This photo sequence will show you some new information.* Read the instructions aloud, or call on individual students to read them. Have students reread silently, if helpful. Help students with new words.

Have students study the photos for a few minutes. Then have pairs of students ask and answer the questions. Tell students to write their answers in their notebooks. Check answers and write them on the board.

**Answers**

**1.** Waves hitting the rocks over and over cause a cave to form. The waves wear away the back of the cave and an arch forms.

**2.** When waves wear away the top of the arch, a tall piece of rock is left.

## Discuss

Read the discussion question aloud. As a class, discuss what will happen to the rock. Ask students how long they think the weathering process will take.

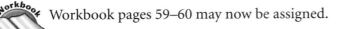 Workbook pages 59–60 may now be assigned.

## Evaluation

### Self-Assessment Questions

Write the following questions on the board. Have students respond in their notebooks. Encourage students to share their responses in small groups or as a class.

1. How can understanding cause and effect help me in reading?
2. How can photo sequences help me understand information?
3. What was difficult for me in this lesson?
4. What was easy for me in this lesson?
5. What was most enjoyable in this lesson?

# Unit Review, pages 124–125

## Warm Up

Have pairs of students list the main ideas from Unit 3. Ask students to use the reading selection headings to group the main ideas. Alternatively, students may organize the main ideas in a word web.

Ask pairs to exchange their completed lists or word webs. Each pair should review the list or word web to see if any important information is missing. If information is missing, the pair should add it.

## Vocabulary

Have students answer questions individually, with a partner, or in small groups, depending on how much support they need. Check answers as a class, as you write the correct answers on the board.

> **Answers**
> 1. Hot liquid rock comes out of the ground when a volcano erupts.
> 2. Igneous rock is made from hot liquid rock.
> 3. Sedimentary rock is made from sand, mud, and tiny pieces of rock.
> 4. Marble is metamorphic rock.
> 5. The study of rocks is called geology.
> 6. Halite is a mineral, also called salt.
> 7. All minerals have properties.
> 8. A large sheet of ice is called a glacier.
> 9. The ground shakes when there is an earthquake.
> 10. The breaking down of rocks is called weathering.
> 11. When wind and water move pieces of rock, it is called erosion.
> 12. A person who studies rocks is called a geologist.

## Check Your Understanding

Have students work individually, with a partner, or in small groups. Check answers as a class, as you write the correct answers on the board.

**Answers**
1. False. Marble and slate are metamorphic rocks.
2. True
3. True
4. False. Rocks can change.
5. True
6. False. Glaciers can move rocks.

## Extension Project

Read the instructions aloud, or call on a student to read them. With the class, take a stroll around or near your school in a location where students are likely to find different types of rocks. Alternatively, assign rock collecting as homework. If you have examples of igneous, sedimentary, and metamorphic rock, allow students to study them again. Then in small groups, ask students to guess what kind of rock they have. Circulate to help and encourage students.

## Apply Science Skills

**Using Visuals: Sectional Diagrams** Read the instructions and diagram labels aloud, or call on a student to read them. Have students reread the instructions and labels silently, if helpful. Write *1–5* on the board as a model. Point to the diagram and ask, *Which label shows what is happening at point 1 in the diagram?* Elicit the answer and write it next to number 1 on the board. Have students complete the exercise in pairs. Check answers as a class.

**Answers**
1. A volcanic eruption brings liquid rock to the surface of the earth.
2. Liquid rock from the volcano cools and hardens.
3. Wind, water, and plants weather the rock and move it downhill into the ocean.
4. The heavy weight of the top layers causes the igneous rock to form sedimentary rock.
5. Hot liquid rock inside the earth melts the sedimentary rock.

## Read More About It

Bring at least one of the suggested books to class. Show the cover and some of the inside pages to students as a preview. Ask students to predict what the book is about. Read an excerpt aloud to the class. Then ask several comprehension questions. Read the excerpt again before calling on students to answer. Encourage students to find this or another suggested book in their school library or local bookstore.

Workbook pages 61–62 may now be assigned.

## Unit Experiment, pages 126–127
### How Do Rocks Change?

### Preview

Begin this section with books closed. Elicit and review the scientific method by asking, *What are the five steps of the scientific method?* Give prompts and hints, if necessary, and write the steps on the board. (Asking questions, Making a hypothesis, Testing a hypothesis, Observing, and Drawing conclusions)

### Do the Experiment

For this experiment, you'll need to have access to a microwave oven. If a microwave oven is not available for class use, you can cook students' models at home. A conventional oven can be used if students use foil instead of plastic wrap.

Depending on what materials and heating methods you use, review with the class any relevant safety tips from pages 14–15 in the Getting Started unit.

Call on a student to read the experiment title aloud. Tell students, *This is our main question.* Ask, *How do rocks change? We can make a model to help us understand.* Read aloud the introduction, purpose, and materials, or have individual students read them. Help students identify all the pictured items on page 126.

Read each of the What to Do instructions aloud, or have a student read them. Ask comprehension questions to make sure students know what to do. Be sure to ask if they have any questions. You may want to control the exercise by reading each step one-by-one and having students complete it. Have students make a hypothesis before or after Step 2. Have students complete their models in pairs or small groups. When students have finished, elicit conclusions from the class and write them on the board while students write them in their logs.

 Workbook page 63 should be used to record the steps during the experiment. Then Workbook page 64 can be assigned.

---

**Answers**
1. We made sedimentary rock because different colors of crayon were layered.
2. We made metamorphic rock because pressure and heat were applied.

---

# Unit 4 Planets and Stars

## Unit Overview

| Lesson | Content | Science Skills | | Experiment |
| --- | --- | --- | --- | --- |
| | | Reading Strategies | Using Visuals | |
| 1 | • The Solar System: the Inner Planets, the Outer Planets, Asteroids and Comets | Reread | Illustrations | How Big Is the Solar System? |
| 2 | • Beyond the Solar System: Constellations, Star Facts | Visualize | Deep Space Photos | |

## Objectives

**Vocabulary**
- Develop new vocabulary related to planets and stars
- Use newly acquired vocabulary in context

**Concepts**
- Learn about the planets in our solar system
- Learn about asteroids, comets, and constellations
- Learn about stars and galaxies in deep space

**Reading Strategies**
- Reread a paragraph to understand and retain information
- Visualize to understand what you read
- Practice previously learned strategies

**Using Visuals**
- Understand how to study illustrations for information
- Understand how to study deep space photos for information

**Experiment**
- Understand the size relationships of the planets

## Unit Opener, pages 128–129

### Preview Topic

Ask students to preview these pages. Then ask, *What is this unit about? What do you think you'll learn about planets and stars?* Ask students what they see in the pictures. Encourage them to say whatever they can. Point to each picture and give a little more information about it.

### Unit Concepts

Read aloud the list of unit concepts for Lessons 1 and 2. Ask, *What words and sentences do you understand?* Elicit information about them and write it on the board. Tell students that they will learn the other information as they read the lessons.

### Get Ready

Read the instructions aloud, or call on individual students to read them. Let students reread silently, if helpful. Point to the illustrations and ask comprehension and picture questions such as, *Is Earth a planet? Where's the sun? How many planets are around the sun?* Say, *Raise your hand if you know the names of other planets.* If many students know planet names, have small groups write down the names they know. Then elicit the names and write them on the board. If few students know planet names, do this activity as a class. (Mercury, Venus, Earth, Mars, Jupiter, Saturn, Uranus, Neptune, Pluto)

## Lesson ❶

## Before You Read, pages 130–133

Have students preview these pages individually or in pairs. Ask, *What will you learn in this lesson?*

### Vocabulary

Read the captions aloud, or call on students to read them. Help students understand and pronounce new words. Use pictures, props, and mime. Have students read the captions again silently. Ask picture and comprehension questions for each caption. Read the key words (page 131) aloud and have students say them after you. Then have students close their books. Point to the pictures and ask questions to elicit the key words.

### Practice

Have students write the sentences in their notebooks, leaving space for each answer. Then have them choose the correct answers and write them in the sentences. Check answers by calling on individual students. Write the letters of the correct answers on the board.

**Answers**

**1.** a. Asteroids     **3.** b. atmosphere     **5.** b. galaxy

**2.** c. orbit           **4.** a. solar system     **6.** c. comet

Workbook page 65 may now be assigned.

## Science Skills

**Science Reading Strategy: Reread** With books closed, ask, *In class, do we usually read a paragraph once or twice? Why do you think we read it twice?* Have students open their books to page 132. Read the heading and introduction aloud or call on individual students to read them. Then have students reread the introduction silently. Ask, *Why do we read the paragraph the first time? Why do we read it again? What are details?*

Read the instructions aloud, or call on a student to read them. Ask, *What does cover mean?* (Model covering your own text.) Have students complete the exercise individually. Elicit answers to the questions and write them on the board. Remind students to read a passage first to understand the most important ideas. Then read it again to understand and remember details.

**Answers**

**1.** The large dark areas are called maria.

**2.** *Maria* means "seas" in Latin. Scientists thought that there were large areas of water on the moon.

**3.** The maria came from volcanoes on the moon's surface.

Workbook page 66 may now be assigned.

**Using Visuals: Illustrations** Have students look at page 130. Hold up your book and point to the picture of the solar system. Say, *This is an illustration. Illustrations give us information.* Ask, *What can you see in this illustration?* (the solar system, planets, the sun, asteroids, the planets are orbiting the sun, the size of the planets, how close they are to the sun) Elicit as much information as you can from students. Ask, *Can we take a photograph of our solar system?* Say, *We make illustrations of things we can't photograph well.*

Have students read the heading at the top of the page. Ask students, *What visuals did you learn about in other units?* (diagrams, cycle diagrams, photographs, pie charts, sectional diagrams, photo sequences) *What visual will you practice using in this lesson?*

Read the introduction, caption, and questions aloud, or call on individual students to read them. Have students reread silently. Ask questions to check understanding and elicit meanings of new words.

Have students study the photo and the illustration for a few minutes. Then have pairs ask and answer the questions. Have them write their answers in their notebooks. Check answers and write them on the board.

**Planets and Stars**    **101**

**Possible Answers**
1. The photo has yellow lines on it. They are the planet's atmosphere. We can't see any mountains. We can't see the surface clearly.
2. Scientists can't take a photo of Venus without the atmosphere because the atmosphere is always there.
3. Venus's surface is red, yellow, and orange. It is rough. There are mountains.

Workbook pages 67–68 may now be assigned.

## Lesson ❶

## The Solar System, pages 134–135

### Preview Pages

Have students preview these pages and predict the topic. Ask, *What are you going to learn on these pages? What do you already know about the solar system?*

### Teach Pages

Read the text and the captions aloud, or call on individual students to read them. Help students with new words. Elicit any key words (galaxy, solar system, orbit), the sentences they are in, and their definitions.

**Understand Information**  Ask, *What is the reading strategy in this lesson? What did you learn when you read the first time? What were the main ideas on these pages?* (Every object you see in the sky is part of the Milky Way galaxy. There are many galaxies in space. The solar system is made up of nine planets. The sun is a star.) Use prompts, if necessary, to elicit the main ideas. Tell students, *Now reread the pages. Try to understand more details.* Have students read the pages again to themselves. Alternatively, have students read aloud to each other in pairs or small groups. Say, *Now I'm going to ask you about the details.* Ask comprehension questions with the students' books open or closed.

**Organize Information**  Have students draw a Cause-and-Effect diagram about gravity and orbits in their notebooks. Write the cause on the board. Then have pairs or groups find the effect and complete their diagrams. The diagram might look like this:

### Orbits and Gravity

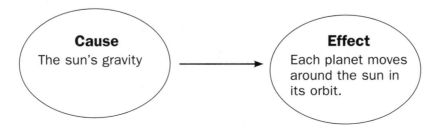

**Cause**
The sun's gravity

**Effect**
Each planet moves around the sun in its orbit.

Draw a T-chart on the board with the categories *Galaxy* and *Solar System*. Say, *Find three key sentences that tell about galaxies. Find three key sentences that tell about solar systems.* Depending on students' abilities, have them do this activity in pairs, in small groups, or as a class. The chart might look like this:

| Solar System | Galaxy |
|---|---|
| A solar system is a group of objects that orbits a star. | A galaxy is a group of stars, planets, gases, and dust. |
| The planets orbit, or move around, the sun. | There are many galaxies in space. |
| The sun's gravity keeps each planet moving in its path, or orbit. | Each galaxy has many solar systems. |

## Language Tip: *Orbit* as a verb/noun

Have students read the text in the Language Tip box. Review the meaning of *verb* and *noun*. Ask for examples. Remind students that they learned in Unit 2 how identical or related words can act as a verb or a noun. (*breathe/breath*) In this case, *orbit* can be both. Have students find sentences with *orbit*. Say, *Is* orbit *a noun or verb in that sentence? How do you know?*

## REACHING ALL STUDENTS: Kinesthetic Learners

Create a total physical response activity about the solar system by having students act out the roles of the sun and nine planets. Arrange nine volunteers in an orbital pattern around another volunteer who plays the sun. Have the rest of the class assign planet names, written on index cards, to the volunteers according to their placement. Demonstrate *counterclockwise* and tell students that planets appear to us to be moving from east to west. Have students move slowly counterclockwise around the sun while Earth also makes one revolution per day.

### Before You Go On

Have pairs of students answer the first two questions. Have them write the questions and answers in their notebooks. Check answers before going on. Answer the third question together as a class.

**Answers**
1. A galaxy is a group of stars, planets, gases, and dust.
2. A solar system is a group of objects that orbits a star.
3. Stars in other galaxies are too far away.

## The Inner Planets, pages 136–137

### Preview Pages

Have students preview the pages and predict what they will learn. Point to the planets and say, *Let's compare and contrast Earth with the other planets on this page.* Remind students that when they compare and contrast, they think about how things are the same and different. Elicit a visual difference by asking, *How is Earth different from Mercury?* Elicit a similarity by asking, *How are Mercury and Earth the same?* Have pairs of students compare and contrast the pictures of the planets. Then elicit some similarities and differences for Venus and Earth, and Mars and Earth.

### Teach Pages

Read the text and the captions aloud, or call on individual students to read them. Help students with new words. Elicit the key word (atmosphere), the sentences it is in, and its definition.

**Understand Information**  Ask, *What were the main ideas on these pages?* (The first four planets are called the inner planets. Mercury is closest to the sun. Venus is hotter than Mercury. Earth is the only planet that we know has life. Mars is farther from the sun than Earth.) Use prompts, if necessary, to elicit the main ideas. Tell students, *Now reread the pages. Try to understand more details.* Have students read the pages again to themselves. Alternatively, have pairs or small groups of students read aloud to each other. Say, *Now I'm going to ask you about the details.* Ask comprehension questions with the students' books open or closed.

**Organize Information**  Have students make a chart listing important information about each inner planet using pages 136–137. Show students how to shorten sentences to write them in the chart. The chart might look like this:

| The Inner Planets | | | |
|---|---|---|---|
| **Mercury** | **Venus** | **Earth** | **Mars** |
| Closest to the sun<br><br>Hot and dry<br><br>Covered with craters<br><br>One-third the size of Earth | Hotter than Mercury<br><br>Clouds of poisonous gases cover the planet<br><br>Thick clouds trap the heat | Only planet with life<br><br>Atmosphere contains oxygen<br><br>Only planet with liquid water<br><br>Water covers 70%<br><br>Called the blue planet | Farther from the sun than Earth<br><br>Colder than Earth<br><br>Reddish, rocky surface<br><br>Called the red planet |

## Language Tip: Comparative and Superlative Adjectives

Read the text in the Language Tip box aloud. Draw a picture of the sun on the board, then three circles labeled Mercury, Venus, and Earth. Ask a student to read aloud the sentences in the Language Tip box again as you point to the appropriate planets. Ask, *Which planet is closer to the sun, Earth or Venus? Which planet is the closest to the sun?* Write *close, closer,* and *closest* on the board. Next to *closer,* write *comparative.* Say, *When we want to compare two things, we use a comparative adjective.* Next to *closest,* write *superlative.* Say, *When we want to compare three or more things, we use a superlative adjective.* Tell students to look for these comparative and superlative adjectives in the reading.

## Science Now: Robots on Mars

Ask students to look at the title and photograph to predict what the text might be about. Ask, *Is this an illustration or a photograph? What do you see in the illustration? What do you see on this robot?*

Read the text aloud, or call on a student to read it. Help students with new words. Ask comprehension questions. Help students locate pictures of rovers on the Internet. Alternatively, download some of these images and bring them to class. Have students discuss what they think we will learn about Mars because of rovers.

## Optional Activity

Teach students a mnemonic device to help memorize the names and order of the nine planets. Write on the board, *My very educated mother just served us nine pizzas.* Underline the first letter of every word. Explain that each underlined letter represents the first letter of a planet in its order from the sun. (Mercury, Venus, Earth, Mars, Jupiter, Saturn, Uranus, Neptune, and Pluto) Have students copy the sentence into their notebooks and practice saying it in pairs several times.

## Before You Go On

Have pairs of students ask the first two questions. Have them write the questions and answers in their notebooks. Check answers before going on. Answer the third question together as a class.

### Answers
1. The inner planets are Mercury, Venus, Earth, and Mars.
2. Venus is the hottest planet because of its atmosphere. Clouds of poisonous gases cover the planet. The thick clouds trap the heat.
3. Possible answers: Earth has a nice atmosphere. It's not too hot or too cold. It has oxygen so animals can live on it. It has clouds, but they're not poisonous.

## The Outer Planets, pages 138–139

### Preview Pages

Have students preview the pages and predict what they will learn. Point to the planets and say, *Let's compare and contrast the pictures of the planets on these pages.* Ask, *What are some things that are the same about these planets? How are they different?* Have pairs of students compare and contrast the pictures of the planets. Then elicit some responses.

### Teach Pages

Read the text and the captions aloud. Help students with new words. Elicit any key words (atmosphere, orbit), the sentences they are in, and their definitions.

**Understand Information** Ask, *What are the main ideas on these pages?* (Jupiter, Saturn, Uranus, Neptune, and Pluto are the outer planets. Jupiter is the largest planet. Saturn is the second-largest planet. Uranus is the seventh planet from the sun. Neptune is about the same size as Uranus. Pluto is the smallest.) Tell students, *Now reread the pages. Try to understand more details.* Ask comprehension questions with the students' books open or closed.

**As You Read:** Reread

Have students read the As You Read box. Ask students to reread the first paragraph on page 139. Then have them close their books and tell you the answer.

**Organize Information** Have students make a chart listing important information about each of the outer planets. The chart might look like this:

| The Outer Planets | | | | |
|---|---|---|---|---|
| **Jupiter** | **Saturn** | **Uranus** | **Neptune** | **Pluto** |
| Fifth planet from the sun<br><br>Largest planet<br><br>11 times the size of Earth<br><br>Atmosphere very windy<br><br>Red spot is giant windstorm<br><br>Rings hard to see | Sixth planet from the sun<br><br>Second-largest planet<br><br>Bright rings easy to see<br><br>Rings made of rock and ice | Seventh planet from the sun<br><br>Half the size of Saturn<br><br>4 times the size of Earth<br><br>Has thin, dark rings | Eighth planet from the sun<br><br>About the same size as Uranus<br><br>Windy atmosphere<br><br>Storms can last hundreds of years | Ninth planet from the sun<br><br>Made of rock and ice<br><br>Smallest, darkest, coldest planet<br><br>Has largest orbit<br><br>From Pluto, the sun looks like a faraway star |

## HISTORY CONNECTION: Neptune, God of the Sea

Ask students to look at the title and illustration to predict what the text might be about. Read the text aloud, or call on a student to read it. Help students with new words. Ask comprehension questions. You may want to bring in pictures of other gods for whom planets are named. Show the pictures to the students and elicit that planet's order from the sun.

## Language Tip: Ordinal Numbers

Have students read the text in the Language Tip box. Tell students, *Four is a cardinal number, and fourth is an ordinal number.* Write *Cardinal* and *Ordinal* on the board. Under *Cardinal*, write the numbers one to fifteen in numerals. Have students copy the numerals into their notebooks. Then elicit the ordinal numbers and write them on the board in letters. Have students copy them. You may also want to show students how ordinals are abbreviated—1st, 2nd, and so on—but tell students they should spell out ordinals when writing for class.

### Before You Go On

Have pairs of students answer the first two questions. Have them write the questions and answers in their notebooks. Check answers before going on. Answer the third question together as a class.

#### Answers
1. Most of the outer planets are made of gases.
2. Pluto is made of rock and ice.
3. Neptune is colder than Jupiter because it's farther from the sun.

## Asteroids and Comets, page 140

### Preview Page

Have students preview this page and predict the topic. Ask, *What are you going to learn on this page?*

### Teach Page

Read the text and the captions aloud, or call on individual students to read them. Help students with new words. Elicit any key words (asteroid, comet, solar system, orbit), the sentences they are in, and their definitions.

**Understand Information** Ask, *What are the main ideas on this page?* (Asteroids are pieces of rock and metal. A comet is a huge mass of ice, frozen gases, and dust.) Use prompts, if necessary, to elicit the main ideas. Tell students, *Now reread the page. Try to understand more details.* Have students read the page again to themselves.

Alternatively, have pairs or small groups of students read aloud to each other. Say, *Now I'm going to ask you about the details.* Ask comprehension questions with the students' books open or closed.

**Organize Information** Have students make a chart listing the important information about asteroids and comets. The chart might look like this:

| Asteroids | Comets |
| --- | --- |
| Pieces of rock or metal | Also orbit the sun |
| Can be very small or hundreds of kilometers wide | Huge masses of ice, frozen gases, and dust |
| Most orbit the sun between Mars and Jupiter | You can see a comet when it's near the sun |
| | The sun heats up the comet and hot gases make a tail |
| | Comets reflect the sun's light |

**Science at Home:** Watching for Comets

Read the text aloud, or call on individual students to read it. Help students with new words. Have students read the pages again to themselves. Alternatively, have students read aloud to each other in pairs or small groups. Ask comprehension and picture questions. You may want to help students find Internet sites about comets. Alternatively, download and bring in pictures of comets to pass out and discuss.

# Exploring, page 141

## Preview Page

Have students preview the page and predict what they will learn. Give students a few minutes to talk about the picture.

## Teach Page

Read the text and the caption aloud, or call on individual students to read them. Help students with new words. Give examples of 10- and 200-kilometer distances (approximately 6 and 124 miles) using landmarks in your community. Have students read the page again to themselves.

**Understand Information** Ask comprehension and picture questions. Then ask critical-thinking questions for students to discuss such as, *Why didn't sunlight reach Earth for months?* (The asteroid made a dark cloud of dust.) *What are two reasons plants died?* (The fires burned them. They couldn't get light.) *What are two reasons the animals and dinosaurs died?* (The fires burned them. They didn't have any food.)

**Organize Information** Ask, *What happened 65 million years ago?* Draw a Cause-and-Effect diagram on the board. Write *An asteroid fell to Earth* in the Cause box. Then ask, *What happened as a result?* Have pairs of students look in the text for the effects on Earth. Elicit the effects and write them in separate boxes on the board. Have students copy the diagram into their notebooks. The diagram might look like this:

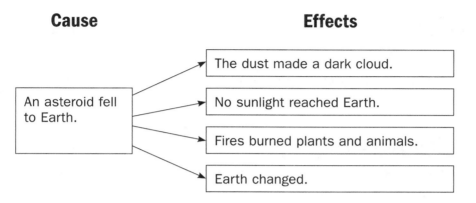

## Cause

An asteroid fell to Earth.

## Effects

The dust made a dark cloud.

No sunlight reached Earth.

Fires burned plants and animals.

Earth changed.

### Before You Go On

Have pairs of students answer the first two questions. Have them write the questions and answers in their notebooks. Check answers before going on. Answer the third question together as a class.

**Answers**
1. An asteroid is a piece of rock or metal.
2. Most of the asteroids in our solar system orbit the sun between Mars and Jupiter.
3. Possible answers: Asteroids and comets both orbit the sun. They are both in our solar system. Neither make their own light. Asteroids are made of rock or metal, but comets are made of ice, frozen gases, and dust. Asteroids can be very small or very big, but comets are always very big. Comets have tails when they're near the sun, but asteroids don't.

For more information, go to www.longmanusa.com/science for links to interesting websites about planets and stars.

# Review and Practice, pages 142–143

## Vocabulary

If students need help in reviewing the vocabulary, see the Optional Vocabulary Activities (pages vii–viii). Have students complete the exercise individually. Check answers as a class.

**Answers**
1. atmosphere
2. galaxy
3. orbit
4. asteroids
5. comet
6. solar system

## Check Your Understanding

Have students answer the questions individually, in pairs, or in small groups. If students need extra support, ask them to look at the information in their notebooks or allow students to look back at the text. Then have students share their answers with the class. Write the answers on the board.

---

**Answers**
1. Mercury and Venus are the two hottest planets.
2. The four inner planets are mostly made of rock.
3. Four of the outer planets are mostly made of gases.
4. Pluto is the coldest planet.

---

## Apply Science Skills

**Science Reading Strategy: Reread** Review the science reading strategy. Ask students, *Why is it important to reread?* Read the instructions or call on a student to read the instructions aloud. Have students copy the questions into their notebooks and individually answer as many as they can without looking at page 141. When students have stopped writing, ask, *How many people need to reread page 141?* Have students close their notebooks, reread the paragraph, and then finish answering the questions. Check answers and write them on the board.

**Using Visuals: Illustrations** Read the instructions and questions aloud, or call on individual students to read them. Help students with new words. Make sure students understand that Pluto is the larger body in the picture. Have students study the illustration for a couple of minutes. Then have pairs ask and answer the questions. Have them write their answers in their notebooks. Check answers and write them on the board.

---

**Possible Answers**
1. You can't see Pluto's surface in the photo. You can see it in the illustration.
2. It is the sun.
3. It is blue and white. It looks like it has red clouds or mountains.

---

## Discuss

Have students discuss the questions in pairs. Then discuss it as a class. Encourage students to offer reasons or examples for their opinions.

Workbook pages 69–70 may now be assigned.

## Evaluation

### Self-Assessment Questions

Write the following questions on the board and have students respond in their notebooks. Encourage students to share their responses in small groups or as a class.

1. How can *rereading* help me in reading?
2. How can illustrations help me understand new ideas?
3. What was difficult for me in this lesson?
4. What was easy for me in this lesson?
5. What was most enjoyable in this lesson?

# Lesson ❷

## Before You Read, pages 144–147

Have students preview these pages individually or in pairs. Ask, *What will you learn in this lesson?*

### Vocabulary

Read the captions, or call on individual students to read them aloud. Help students understand and pronounce new words. Use pictures, props, and mime. Have students read the captions again silently. Ask picture and comprehension questions for each item. Review large numbers with students. Write these numbers and their names on the board and help students pronounce them: *1,000 = one thousand, 1,000,000 = one million, 1,000,000,000 = one billion, 1,000,000,000,000 = one trillion.* Have students copy the numbers and names into their notebooks.

Read the key words (page 145) aloud and have students say them after you. Then have students close their books. Point to the pictures and ask questions to elicit the key words.

### Practice

Read the instructions aloud. Elicit one or more definitions, if helpful. Have pairs or small groups of students define the words. Check by calling on individual students to read their sentences. Write the definitions on the board.

> **Possible Answers**
> - astronomers: scientists who study planets, stars, and galaxies
> - constellation: a group of stars that makes a pattern
> - telescope: a tool scientists use to see other planets, stars, and galaxies
> - trillion: the number 1,000,000,000,000
> - universe: space and everything in it; the many galaxies and stars in space

 Workbook page 71 may now be assigned.

## Science Skills

**Science Reading Strategy: Visualize** Write *Visualize* on the board. Tell students, *When we visualize, we make pictures in our minds while we read.* Tell students to close their eyes. Tell them to imagine pictures as they listen to you read. Read the paragraph about Mars on page 137. Pause a few seconds after each sentence. Have students open their eyes. Ask, *What did you see? What words helped you see that?*

Read aloud the information at the top of page 146, or call on a student to read it. Ask, *What is this boy in the picture doing? What is he visualizing?* Write the new words *circle around*, *pathway*, and *squashed circles* on the board. Help students understand and pronounce them before they read the paragraph. Read the paragraph aloud. Pause after each sentence and ask, *Did you visualize? Did you see a picture in your mind?* Have pairs or small groups of students discuss the three questions. Then elicit answers from different students.

---

**Possible Answers**
1. The sun is in the center. Nine planets circle around it in space.
2. They are almost round, like squashed circles.
3. objects in space, in the center, the sun, pathway, orbit, almost round, squashed circles.

---

Workbook pages 72–73 may now be assigned.

**Using Visuals: Deep Space Photos** Have students look at page 145. Hold up your book and point to the picture of the galaxies. Say, *This is a photograph of part of the universe. A telescope in space took this photo. The telescope orbits Earth. It can take pictures of stars and galaxies. These stars and galaxies are very far from Earth and the solar system. We call space outside the solar system* deep space. Write *deep space* on the board. Have students look at the photograph of the galaxy on pages 128–129. Say, *This is a deep space photo of a galaxy. What can you see in this galaxy? What colors can you see in this galaxy? What shapes can you see?*

Have students read the heading at the top of page 147. Ask, *What visuals did you learn about in other lessons?* (diagrams, cycle diagrams, photographs, pie charts, sectional diagrams, photo sequences, illustrations) *What visual will you practice using in this lesson?*

Read the introduction and captions aloud, or call on individual students to read them. Have students reread silently. Ask questions to check understanding. Have students study the photo of deep space for a few minutes. Then have pairs ask and answer the questions. Have students write their answers in their notebooks. Check by eliciting answers and writing them on the board.

---

**Possible Answers**
1. The hottest stars are blue. The coolest stars are red.
2. Red, orange, yellow, white, and blue
3. Yes. You can see a star of each color in the photo.

---

Workbook page 74 may now be assigned.

# Lesson ②

## Beyond the Solar System, pages 148–149

**Preview Pages**

Have students preview the pages and predict what they will learn.

**Teach Pages**

Read the text and the captions aloud, or call on individual students to read them. Help students with new words. Elicit any key words (universe, trillion, telescope [in caption]), the sentences they are in, and their definitions.

**Understand Information** Tell students to read the pages again to themselves. Say, *Visualize as you read. Stop for a few seconds after each sentence. Visualize a picture in your mind.* After students have finished reading, ask, *What pictures did you visualize? What words helped you see the pictures?* Have students discuss their mental pictures. Then ask comprehension and picture questions.

**Organize Information** Tell students, *Now you'll make a diagram comparing the sun, a galaxy, and the universe.* Have students copy the diagram as you draw it on the board. Draw a circle on the board and write inside the circle *The sun = ____ star.* Draw a larger circle around the first and write inside it *A galaxy = _____ s of stars.* Finally, draw a larger circle around the last one and write *The universe = _____ s of galaxies, _____ of stars.* Say, *Make a guess. Write numbers in the blanks.* The diagram might look like this:

## The Universe

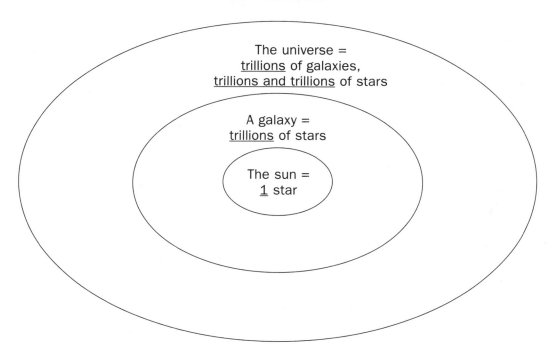

**Language Tip:** Contraction: *it's*

Review contractions with pronouns and the verb *to be*. List the pronouns and elicit the correct form of *be* for each pronoun. Show students how to make a contraction. Point to the Language Tip box and read the text aloud or have a student read it. Ask students to find the sentence with *it's* on page 149. Have students make new sentences using *it's*.

## REACHING ALL STUDENTS: Visual Learners

Use the photo of the planets on page 148 to review information. Point to the planets and say, *One of these is not a planet. Can you tell which one?* (the moon) *How can you tell?* (It's white, there are dark maria, and it's near Earth.) *How many planets can you see in the photo?* (eight) Point to the inner planets and ask, *What are these planets? How many inner planets are there? What are they?* Point to the outer planets. *What are these planets? How many are there?* (four in the picture, but really there are five) *What planets can you see?* (Jupiter, Saturn, Neptune, Uranus) *What planet is missing?* (Pluto) *Why do you think it's missing?* (It's hard to take a photo of it.)

### Before You Go On

Have pairs of students answer the first two questions. Have them write the questions and answers in their notebooks. Check answers before going on. Answer the third question together as a class.

**Answers**
1. The universe is (a name for) everything in space, including planets, stars, and galaxies.
2. There are perhaps a trillion trillion.
3. Possible answers: Most of the stars we see look white. They aren't so bright or so big.

## Constellations, pages 150–151

### Preview Pages

Have students preview the pages and predict what they will learn. Have pairs of students compare and contrast the pictures of Ursa Major (the Great Bear) and Orion.

### Teach Pages

Read the text and the captions aloud, or call on individual students to read them. Help students with new words. Elicit the key word (constellation), the sentences it is in, and its definition.

**Understand Information** Tell students to read the pages again to themselves. Say, *Visualize as you read. Stop for a few seconds after each sentence. Visualize a picture* *in your mind.* After students have finished reading, ask, *What pictures did you visualize? What words helped you see those pictures?* Have students discuss their mental pictures. Then have students develop their own questions about the reading and work in pairs to ask and answer them. Follow up with your own comprehension and picture questions.

**Organize Information** Have students make a Main Idea and Details chart for the second paragraph on page 150. You may want to elicit the main idea and write it on the board before students begin. The chart might look like this:

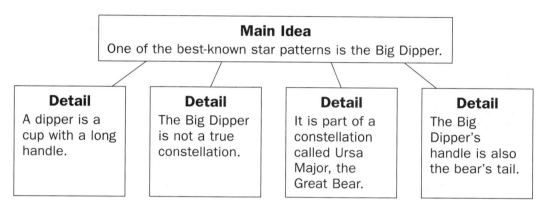

**Main Idea**
One of the best-known star patterns is the Big Dipper.

**Detail**
A dipper is a cup with a long handle.

**Detail**
The Big Dipper is not a true constellation.

**Detail**
It is part of a constellation called Ursa Major, the Great Bear.

**Detail**
The Big Dipper's handle is also the bear's tail.

Later, have students make a Main Idea and Details chart about Orion.

---

**Language Tip:** Adverbs: *well/better/best*

Review what students have learned about comparative and superlative adjectives and adverbs. Read the text in the Language Tip box aloud or have a volunteer read it. Point out that *well* is an adverb that describes a verb. For example, *I know him well. Good* is an adjective that describes a noun. *Good* and *well* are irregular. They have the same comparative and superlative forms. Model sentences using each form and ask students to give additional examples.

---

## Optional Activity

Have students make a class book of constellations. Each student can contribute one page to the book by researching, drawing, and writing about one constellation.

---

**Science at Home:** Antares and Scorpio

Ask students to look at the title and illustration to predict what the text might be about. Ask, *What animal do you see in this illustration? What color stars do you see in the illustration? Which is cooler, a white star or a red star?*

Read the text aloud, or call on a student to read it. Help students with new words. Ask comprehension questions. Have students write *Antares* and where they should look for it in their notebooks. Encourage students to look for this star as homework, if students are in an area where they can easily and safely observe stars and if Antares will be visible. Alternatively, if the Big Dipper, Ursa Major, or Orion can be seen, you may want to have students look for them.

Have pairs of students answer the first two questions. Have them write the questions and answers in their notebooks. Check answers before going on. Answer the third question together as a class.

**Answers**
1. A constellation is a star pattern.
2. The Big Dipper is one of the best-known star patterns. It is part of a constellation called Ursa Major.
3. Answers will vary.

## Star Facts, pages 152–153

### Preview Pages

Have students preview the pages and predict what they will learn.

### Teach Pages

Read the text and captions aloud, or call on individual students to read them. Help students with new words. There are no key words on these pages.

**Understand Information** Tell students to read the pages again to themselves. Say, *Visualize as you read. Stop for a few seconds after each sentence. Visualize a picture in your mind.* After students have finished reading, ask, *What pictures did you visualize? What words helped you see those pictures?* Have students discuss their mental pictures. Then have students develop their own questions about the reading and work in pairs to ask and answer them. Follow up with your own comprehension and picture questions.

**Organize Information** Have pairs of students make a Main Idea and Details chart for the last paragraph on page 153 about the size of stars. Check answers by calling on students to complete a chart on the board. Each student can fill in one part of the chart.

---

**Language Tip:** *Bright/Brightness*

Remind students about word families. Word families are related words from the same root. Read the text in the Language Tip box aloud or ask a volunteer to read it. Have students find a sentence on page 152 that has the word *bright*. (in the caption under Environment Watch) Then have students find a sentence that has *brightness*. (in the text) Ask students to find other words on page 152 that are in the same word family. (brighter, brightest) You may want to review comparative and superlative adjectives using *bright*, *brighter*, and *brightest*. Have students create sentences using each word form.

---

**Environment Watch**: Light Pollution

Ask students to look at the title and photograph to predict what the text might be about. Read the text aloud, or call on a student to read it. Help students with new words. Ask comprehension questions. Discuss light pollution with the class. Ask, *Do we have light pollution in our town? Do you think the city should change the light bulbs in our street lamps? What other things cause light pollution? What can we do?*

**ART CONNECTION**: Antoni Gaudí, Architect

Ask students to look at the title and photograph to predict what the text might be about. Ask, *What kind of building is this? Does it look like most churches? Do you like it?* Read the text aloud, or call on a student to read it. Help students with new words. Ask comprehension questions. Bring in a book with pictures of other work by Gaudí, or find pictures on the Internet. Have students look at these pictures and discuss which buildings they like and why.

**Before You Go On**

Have pairs of students answer all three questions. Have them write the questions and answers in their notebooks. Check answers before going on.

**Answers**
1. Because the sun's brightness overpowers the brightness of other stars.
2. The sun looks brighter than Sirius because the sun is much closer to us.
3. Sirius is hotter than the sun because it is a blue-white color.

## Star Facts (continued), pages 154–155

### Preview Pages

Have students preview the pages and predict what they will learn. Ask students to summarize, or retell, what they learned about stars on pages 152–153.

### Teach Pages

Read the text and the captions aloud, or call on individual students to read them. Help students with new words. Elicit any key words (telescope, astronomers), the sentences they are in, and their definitions.

**Understand Information** Tell students to read the pages again to themselves. Say, *Visualize as you read. Stop for a few seconds after each sentence. Visualize a picture in your mind.* After students have finished reading, ask, *What pictures did you visualize? What words helped you see the pictures?* Have students discuss their mental pictures. Then have students develop their own questions about the reading and work in pairs to ask and answer them. Follow up with your own comprehension and picture questions.

## As You Read: Visualize

Read the text in the As You Read box. Ask students to respond to the question. Make a list of the words on the board.

**Organize Information** Have students do a sequence diagram of the star life cycle on page 154. The diagram might look like this:

## The Star Life Cycle

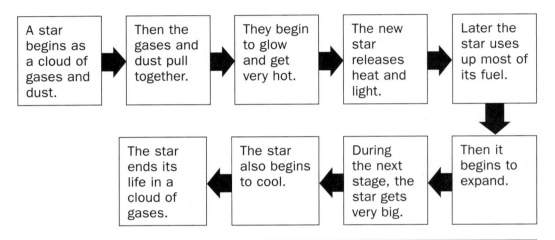

A star begins as a cloud of gases and dust. → Then the gases and dust pull together. → They begin to glow and get very hot. → The new star releases heat and light. → Later the star uses up most of its fuel. → Then it begins to expand. → During the next stage, the star gets very big. → The star also begins to cool. → The star ends its life in a cloud of gases.

## Leaders in Science: Edwin Hubble

Read the title, then point to the pictures and ask, *Who is this man? You saw this tool before. What is it? What does it take pictures of?* Read the text and the captions aloud, or call on individual students to read them. Have students read the text again to themselves. Ask comprehension questions. You may want to help students find Internet sites with Hubble photos.

### Before You Go On

Have pairs of students answer the first two questions. Have them write the questions and answers in their notebooks. Check answers before going on. Answer the third question together as a class.

**Answers**
1. A star begins its life as a cloud of gases and dust.
2. Galaxies are usually either elliptical or spiral.
3. The Hubble Space Telescope helped us see different galaxies. It can see things very far away.

Websites

For more information, go to www.longmanusa.com/science for links to interesting websites about planets and stars.

# Review and Practice, pages 156–157

## Vocabulary

If students need help reviewing the vocabulary, see the Optional Vocabulary Activities (pages vii–viii). Have students complete the exercise individually. Check answers as a class.

**Answers**
1. Telescope
2. constellation
3. universe
4. trillion
5. astronomer

## Check Your Understanding

Have students answer the questions individually, in pairs, or in small groups. If students need extra support, tell them to look at the information in their notebooks or allow students to look back at the text. Then have students share their answers with the class. Write the answers on the board.

**Answers**
1. A star ends its life in a cloud of gases.
2. Constellations are star patterns.
3. The hottest color of stars is blue. The coolest color is red.
4. The other stars don't look as bright as the sun because they are farther away than the sun.

## Apply Science Skills

**Science Reading Strategy: Visualize** Ask students, *How do you visualize? How does this help you understand?*

Read the instructions and the paragraph aloud, or have a student read them. Tell students to read the paragraph once more and draw a picture of what they visualized. Have students complete their drawings individually. Allow time for students to share what they have drawn. Ask, *What words helped you visualize that?*

**Using Visuals: Deep Space Photos** Tell students, *You learned about deep space photos in this lesson. This Hubble Space Telescope photo will show you some new information.* Read the instructions aloud, or call on individual students to read them. Have students reread silently, if helpful. Ask comprehension questions to review concepts. Have students study the photo and the enlarged inset for a few moments. Encourage students to look back at the illustrations of spiral and elliptical galaxies on page 155, if helpful. Have students point out the galaxies to a classmate. Hold up your book and point to them so that all students can see.

## Discuss

Read the discussion questions aloud. Encourage students to look back at their diagram of the number of stars in the universe. Discuss the two questions as a class. Take a class vote on how many students believe that there are other planets like Earth. Have students synthesize what they have learned in science through a discussion of the second question. Students may summarize the discussion for homework.

 Workbook pages 75–76 may now be assigned.

## Evaluation

### Self-Assessment Questions

Write the following questions on the board. Have students respond in their notebooks. Encourage students to share their responses in small groups or as a class.
1. How can visualizing help me in reading?
2. How can deep space photos help me understand information?
3. What was difficult for me in this lesson?
4. What was easy for me in this lesson?
5. What was most enjoyable in this lesson?

# Unit Review, pages 158–159

## Warm Up

Have pairs of students list the main ideas in Unit 4. Ask students to use the reading selection headings to group the main ideas. Alternatively, students may organize the main ideas in a web. Ask pairs to exchange their completed lists or word webs. Each pair should review their newly acquired list to see if any important information is missing. If information is missing, the pair should add it.

## Vocabulary

Have students answer questions individually, with a partner, or in small groups. Check answers as a class as you write the answers on the board.

> ### Answers
> 1. The Milky Way is a galaxy.
> 2. The universe is everything in space.
> 3. The atmosphere is the layer of gases around Earth.
> 4. Earth, eight other planets, and the sun make up the solar system.
> 5. A planet's path around the sun is called an orbit.
> 6. A person who studies objects in space is called an astronomer.
> 7. Pieces of rock and metal in space are called asteroids.
> 8. A comet is made of ice and dust, and has a tail.
> 9. The number 1,000,000,000,000 is one trillion.
> 10. Ursa Major is a constellation.
> 11. Scientists use telescopes to see planets, stars, and galaxies.

## Check Your Understanding

Have students work individually, with a partner, or in small groups, depending on how much support they need. Check answers as a class, as you write the correct answers on the board.

**Answers**
1. True
2. False. The four inner planets are made mostly of rock.
3. False. Most of the outer planets are made mostly of gases and liquids.
4. True
5. False. Blue stars are hotter than red stars.
6. True

## Extension Project

Read the instructions aloud, or call on a student to read them. Ask students to think of a planet they're interested in learning more about. Alternatively, assign planets so that each one is represented. Have students research their planet individually, with a partner, or in small groups. Allow class time for students to present their posters.

## Apply Science Skills

**Using Visuals: Deep Space Photos** Read the instructions aloud, or call on a student to read them. Have students answer the questions individually, in pairs, or in small groups. Check answers as a class.

**Answers**
1. The two stars look very similar. They both have rings.
2. The rings are made of gases.

## Read More About It

Bring at least one of the suggested books to class. Show the cover and some of the inside pages to students as a preview. Ask students to predict what the book is about. Read an excerpt aloud to the class. Then ask several comprehension questions. Read the excerpt again before calling on students to answer. Encourage students to find this or another suggested book in their school library or local bookstore.

 Workbook pages 77–78 may now be assigned.

# Unit Experiment, pages 160–161
## How Big Is the Solar System?

**Preview**

Call on a student to read the experiment question. Have students predict what they might be doing. Read aloud the introduction, purpose, and materials, or have individual students read them. Help students with new words. Make sure students understand what the experiment is about.

**Do the Experiment**

Read each of the What to Do instructions aloud, or have a student read them. Review the data table. Ask comprehension questions to make sure that students know what to do and that they understand the table. Be sure to ask if they have any questions. You may want to assign making appropriate-sized models of planets and measuring distances to different pairs or groups, or do the experiment as a class. When the experiment has been completed, elicit conclusions from the class and write them on the board while students write them in their logs.

Below is a metric conversion chart to help those students who are not familiar with the metric system.

| | | |
|---|---|---|
| 1 mile | = | 1.6 kilometers |
| 1 kilometer | = | .62 miles |
| 1 inch | = | 2.5 centimeters |
| 1 centimeter | = | .39 inches |

 Have students use workbook page 79 for writing up and drawing conclusions about the experiment. Workbook page 80 may then be assigned.

# Unit 5 Matter

## Unit Overview

| Lesson | Content | Science Skills | | Experiment |
| | | Reading Strategies | Using Visuals | |
|---|---|---|---|---|
| 1 | • What Is Matter?<br>• Properties: Mass, Volume, Density<br>• What Makes Up Matter? | Facts and Examples | Micrographs | Can You Observe Density? |
| 2 | • States of Matter: Solids, Liquids, Gases<br>• Changing States of Matter<br>• Physical and Chemical Changes | Idea Maps | States of Matter Illustrations | |

## Objectives

### Vocabulary
• Develop new vocabulary related to matter
• Use newly acquired vocabulary in context

### Concepts
• Learn about matter and its properties
• Learn about the three states of matter
• Learn about physical and chemical changes to matter

### Reading Strategies
• Understand facts and examples in a text to improve comprehension
• Draw an idea map to understand and remember what you read
• Practice previously learned strategies

### Using Visuals
• Understand how to study micrographs for information
• Understand how to study states of matter illustrations for information

### Experiment
• Observe density in liquids and solids

# Unit Opener, pages 162–163

## Preview Topic

Ask students to preview these pages. Then ask, *What is this unit about? What do you think you'll learn about matter?* Ask students what they see in the pictures. Encourage them to say whatever they can. Point to each picture and give a little more information about it.

### Unit Concepts

Read aloud the list of unit concepts for Lessons 1 and 2. Ask, *What words and sentences do you understand?* Elicit information about them and write it on the board. Tell students they will learn the other information as they read the lessons.

### Get Ready

Read the instructions aloud, or call on individual students to read them. Have students copy the chart into their notebooks. Make sure students know what wood, metal, plastic, and glass are. Show examples or pictures, if possible. Elicit the name of one classroom object in each category. Then have pairs of students write as many objects as they can in each category. Check answers as a class. Count the overall number of objects in each category.

# Lesson ❶

# Before You Read, pages 164–167

Have students preview these pages individually or in pairs. Ask, *What will you learn in this lesson?*

## Vocabulary

Read the captions aloud, or call on individual students to read them. Help students understand and pronounce new words. Use pictures, props, and mime. Have students read the captions again silently.

Ask picture and comprehension questions for each item. Read the key words (page 165) aloud and have students say them after you. Then have students close their books. Point to the pictures and ask questions to elicit the key words.

### Practice

Have students write the sentences in their notebooks, choose answers, and write the words in the sentences. Check answers as a class. Write the letters of the correct answers on the board.

### Answers
**1.** b. mass      **3.** a. density      **5.** c. Volume
**2.** c. atoms      **4.** b. measure      **6.** a. matter

Workbook page 81 may now be assigned.

## Science Skills

**Science Reading Strategy: Facts and Examples** With books closed, write *Facts* and *Examples* on the board and tell students, *A fact is a main science idea. Examples help us understand facts.* Say, *You can measure volume with a measuring cup. This is a fact. For example, you can measure the volume of water with a measuring cup. This is an example.*

Have students open their books to page 166. Read the heading and introduction aloud, or call on students to read them. Help students understand new words like *suppose.* Say, Suppose *means "imagine."* Read the paragraph aloud, or call on individual students to read it. Help students with comprehension and new words. Let students reread the paragraph, and then focus their attention on the first Fact and Example diagram. Have students find this information in the text. Ask, *What words introduced the example?* (for example) Tell students to copy the second Fact and Example diagram in their notebooks and complete it. Elicit the answer and write it on the board.

Workbook pages 82–83 may now be assigned.

**Using Visuals: Micrographs** Have students read the heading at the top of page 167. Ask students, *What visuals did you learn about in other units?* (diagrams, cycle diagrams, photographs, pie charts, sectional diagrams, photo sequences, illustrations, deep space photos) *What visual will you practice using in this lesson?*

Review the word *microscope* by having students look back at page 19 and saying, *Microscopes let scientists see very small things.* Then have students look at the micrograph of atoms in sand on page 165. Hold up your book and point to the micrograph. Say, *This is a micrograph. Micrographs are photos taken with a microscope. Micrographs give us information.* Ask, *Do you see the atoms in this micrograph?* (yes) *Can you see atoms in sand with your eyes?* (no, they're too small) *Micrographs let us see very small things.*

Read the introduction, captions, and questions, or call on individual students to read them aloud. Ask questions to check understanding and elicit meanings of vocabulary.

Have students study the micrographs for a few minutes. Then have pairs ask and answer the questions. Have them write their answers in their notebooks. Check answers as a class and write them on the board.

### Answers
**1.** Sand is a mixture of different kinds of matter.
**2.** The snowflake, sugar, and salt are made of only one kind of matter.
**3.** The micrograph of salt shows the mineral halite.

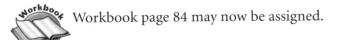 Workbook page 84 may now be assigned.

## Lesson ➊

# What Is Matter? pages 168–175
## Properties, pages 168–170

### Preview Pages

Have students preview these pages and predict the topic. Ask, *What are you going to learn on these pages? What do you already know about matter?*

### Teach Pages

Read the text and the captions aloud, or call on individual students to read them. Help students with new words. Elicit any key words (matter, mass), the sentences they are in, and their definitions.

Have students read the pages again to themselves. Alternatively, have students read aloud to each other in pairs or small groups. Remind students to use the reading strategies they have learned in other units to help them understand. Have pairs of students ask each other questions about the reading. Follow up with your own comprehension and picture questions.

> **Language Tip:** Multiple Meanings: *Space*
>
> Have students read the text in the Language Tip box. Remind them of how *space* was used in Unit 4. Then ask them to show you the space around them by gesturing. Ask students if they can think of any other contexts in which we use the word *space*. (a space between words, leave space on a page, space in a room, and so on)

**Understand Information** Ask, *What is the reading strategy in this lesson? How do examples help us?* Say, *Look at the first paragraph on page 168. What are some facts about matter? What are some examples? What are some facts about mass? What is an example?* Have students reread the text to locate the facts and examples. Continue in the same manner until all the facts and examples have been located on both pages. Ask comprehension and picture questions.

**Organize Information** Have students look again at the first paragraph on page 168. Say, *Let's make a fact and example diagram about matter.* Work with the class to make a diagram on the board. Have students copy it into their notebooks. The diagram might look like this:

# Matter

```
┌─────────────────────────────────┐
│             Facts               │              ⎛   Example    ⎞
│ Everything you see is matter.   │             ⎜ Matter can be a ⎟
│ Matter can be living or         │─────────────⎜ book, a cloud, or⎟
│ nonliving. Matter is anything   │             ⎜ a person.       ⎟
│ that takes up space and has mass.│             ⎝                ⎠
└─────────────────────────────────┘
```

Then, individually or in pairs, have students make another fact and example diagram about mass.

## REACHING ALL STUDENTS: Kinesthetic Learners

Bring in a piece of wood and a container of honey. Have students pass them around. Encourage them to look at, smell, and touch both. Elicit the properties of wood and honey, both those in the text and others that students find. Do this exercise orally, because students will do an idea map of this section in the next lesson.

### Before You Go On

Have pairs of students answer the first two questions. Have them write the questions and answers in their notebooks. Check answers before going on. Answer the third question together as a class.

**Answers**
1. Matter is anything that takes up space and has mass.
2. Wood is hard. Most types of wood float on water. Wood burns easily.
3. Possible answers: sugar, salt, drink mix, pancake syrup, soap, toothpaste

**Mass, page 170**
**Volume, page 171**

### Preview Pages

Have students preview these pages and predict the topic. Ask, *What are you going to learn on these pages?*

### Teach Pages

Read the text and the captions aloud, or call on individual students to read them. Help students with new words. Elicit any key words (matter, measure, mass, volume), the sentences they are in, and their definitions.

Have students read the pages again to themselves. Alternatively, have pairs or small groups of students read aloud to each other. Remind students to use the reading strategies they have learned in other units to help them understand. Have pairs of students ask each other questions about the reading. Follow up with your own comprehension and picture questions.

**Understand Information** Ask, *What is the reading strategy in this lesson? How do examples help us?*

**As You Read:** Facts and Examples

Have students read the text in the As You Read box. Ask pairs of students to look for examples of containers in the pictures on pages 170–171. Check answers as a class. (a two-liter container, a glass measuring cup, a container of oil, a metal cup)

**Organize Information** Have students make a Fact and Example diagram for the first paragraph on page 170. Elicit the fact before students begin, if helpful. The diagram might look like this:

### Properties and Senses

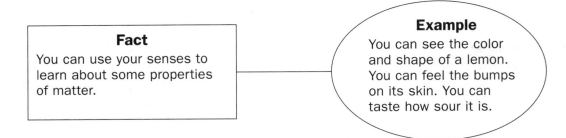

**Fact**
You can use your senses to learn about some properties of matter.

**Example**
You can see the color and shape of a lemon. You can feel the bumps on its skin. You can taste how sour it is.

**Science at Home:** Measuring Matter

Ask students to look at the title and predict what the text might be about. Read the text aloud, or call on a student to read it. Ask comprehension questions. Tell students to look for measuring containers at home and write their observations for homework.

**Language Tip:** *Contain/Container*

Have students read the text in the Language Tip box. Write *contain* ⟶ *verb* and *container* ⟶ *noun* on the board and have students write the lines in their notebooks. Ask, *How is the noun made?* (You add *-er.*) Underline *-er* and say, *This is a suffix.* Write *suffix* and *-er* on the board. Say, *We put suffixes at the end of a word to change its meaning.*

Have pairs of students answer the first two questions. Have them write the questions and answers in their notebooks. Check answers before going on. Answer the third question together as a class.

   After the third question, have students discuss how they could measure the volume of a rock. (Put a rock into a cup, then fill the cup to the top with water. Take out the rock. The volume of the rock is the amount of space in the cup.) Demonstrate for students, if helpful.

**Answers**
1. You use a balance to measure mass.
2. Volume is the amount of space something takes up.
3. Water is easier to measure because it takes the shape of its container. A rock doesn't.

# Exploring, page 172

## Preview Page

Have students preview the page and predict what they will learn.

## Teach Page

Read the text aloud, or call on individual students to read it. Help students with new words. Elicit the key word (measure), the sentence it is in, and the definition.

   Have students read the page again to themselves. Alternatively, have students read aloud to each other in pairs or small groups. Remind students to use the reading strategies they have learned in other units to help them understand. Have pairs of students ask each other questions about the reading. Follow up with your own comprehension and picture questions.

**Understand Information** Ask, *What is the reading strategy in this lesson? How do examples help us?* Say, *Let's read about* Measurement in History *again and look for facts and examples.* Have students reread the text to locate the facts and examples.

**Organize Information** In pairs, have students make Fact and Example diagrams to represent the information on this page. (There is no example for the Romans' use of the pound.) Students' diagrams might look like this:

## Measurement in History

**Facts**

**Examples**

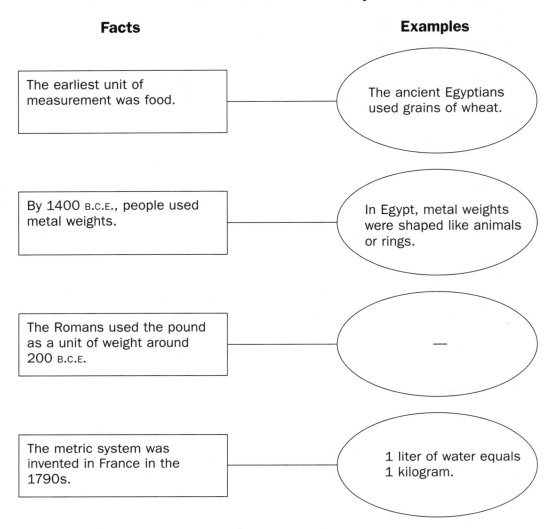

| Facts | Examples |
|-------|----------|
| The earliest unit of measurement was food. | The ancient Egyptians used grains of wheat. |
| By 1400 B.C.E., people used metal weights. | In Egypt, metal weights were shaped like animals or rings. |
| The Romans used the pound as a unit of weight around 200 B.C.E. | — |
| The metric system was invented in France in the 1790s. | 1 liter of water equals 1 kilogram. |

## Optional Activity

If you have access to a balance, teach students how to use it. Call on several students to find the mass of different items such as a rock, a bottle of water, a piece of wood, or a lemon. Have the class record each item and its mass in their notebooks.

---

**Density, page 173**

---

### Preview Page

Have students preview the page and predict what they will learn.

### Teach Page

Read the text and the captions aloud, or call on individual students to read them. Help students with new words. Elicit any key words (measure, density, mass, volume), the sentences they are in, and their definitions.

Have students read the page again to themselves. Alternatively, have pairs of students read aloud to each other. Remind students to use the reading strategies they have learned in other units to help them understand. Have pairs ask each other questions about the reading. Follow up with your own comprehension and picture questions.

---

**Language Tip:** *per* = for each

Have students read the text in the Language Tip box. Ask them to find *per unit* in the text, read the sentence, and explain what it means in their own words. Remind students that they already know *percent* from Unit 2. Have students turn back to Unit 2 and find where *percent* was used. (pie charts, page 79)

---

**Understand Information** Ask, *What is the reading strategy in this lesson?* Have students reread the text and find facts about density and an example. If possible, demonstrate the example of measuring the mass of pennies and puffed rice.

---

**MATH CONNECTION:** Measuring Density

Ask students to look at the title and the equation and predict what the text might be about. Read the text aloud, or call on a student to read it. Ask comprehension questions. Have students write the equation in their notebooks. Then have them write the equation for water using the same format.

---

**Organize Information** Do the Math Connection first. Then have students make a chart about mass, volume, and density using the information on pages 170, 171, and 173. Have students supply the information for mass, if helpful. The chart might look like this:

| Properties | | |
|---|---|---|
| **Mass** | **Volume** | **Density** |
| Mass is like weight.<br><br>You measure the mass of something by using a balance. | Volume is the amount of space something takes up.<br><br>You use containers of different sizes to measure volume. | Density is the amount of mass a certain volume of something has.<br><br>First you find out the mass and the volume. Then you divide the mass by the volume. |

## Optional Activity

To provide a hands-on experience, bring one or more balances and liter measuring cups or containers to class. First have students use the balance to measure the mass of the empty measuring cup or container. Then have students measure equal volumes of different substances, such as water, flour, sugar, milk, pennies, or cereal. Have them weigh each volume and report their results. Make sure they subtract the weight of the measuring cup. Then have them figure out the density of each item.

Have pairs of students answer the first two questions. Have them write the questions and answers in their notebooks. Check answers before going on. Answer the third question together as a class.

Display a cotton ball and a rock to provide visual clues to the answer.

**Answers**
1. Density is how much matter there is in a certain amount of space.
2. Pennies have more density than puffed rice.
3. A rock has greater density than a cotton ball.

## What Makes Up Matter? pages 174–175

**Preview Pages**

Have students preview the pages and predict what they'll learn.

**Teach Pages**

Read the text and the captions aloud, or call on individual students to read them. Help students with new words. Elicit any key words (matter, atoms), the sentences they are in, and their definitions.

Have students read the pages again to themselves. Alternatively, have pairs of students read aloud to each other. Remind students to use the reading strategies they have learned in other units to help them understand. Have pairs of students ask each other questions about the reading. Follow up with your own comprehension and picture questions.

**Understand Information**  Point to the photos of the salad and the sugar, and for each ask, *What's this?* Say, *Let's compare and contrast the salad and the sugar.* Have pairs of students discuss the similarities and differences, and then make a Venn diagram in their notebooks. Ask, *What are some things that are the same about them?* (Both are edible, both are composed of atoms, and both are from things you grow.) *How are they different from each other?* (Sugar is a pure substance; the salad is a mixture. Refined sugar is made of small grains; salad is a mixture of vegetables or fruits.)

**Organize Information**  Have students make Fact and Example diagrams for pure substances and mixtures using information on page 174. If helpful, elicit a fact about a pure substance before students begin. The diagrams might look like this:

### Pure Substances

| **Fact** | **Example** |
|---|---|
| A pure substance is made of only one type of matter. | Salt and sugar are examples of pure substances. |

## Mixtures

**Fact**

A mixture is made of several types of matter.

**Example**

Sand is an example of a mixture. Another example of a mixture is a salad.

**Before You Go On**

Have pairs of students answer the first two questions. Have them write the questions and answers in their notebooks. Check answers before going on. Answer the third question together as a class.

**Answers**

1. A pure substance is made of only one type of matter.
2. Matter is made up of tiny pieces called atoms.
3. Possible answers: a cake mix, taco seasoning, chocolate milk, prepared foods

For more information, go to www.longmanusa.com/science for links to interesting websites about matter.

# Review and Practice, pages 176–177

## Vocabulary

If students need help in reviewing the vocabulary, see the Optional Vocabulary Activities (pages vii–viii). Have students complete the exercise individually. Check answers as a class.

**Answers**

| | | |
|---|---|---|
| 1. measure | 3. volume | 5. density |
| 2. atoms | 4. mass | 6. matter |

## Check Your Understanding

Have students answer the questions individually, in pairs, or in small groups. If students need extra support, tell them to look at the information in their notebooks or allow students to look back at the text. Then have students share their answers with the class. Write the answers on the board.

**Answers**

1. Matter is anything that takes up space and has mass.
2. Possible answers: You can use your senses to learn about matter's properties. You can measure matter to learn about mass, volume, and density.
3. You use containers to measure the volume of something.
4. Water has greater density than air. They have the same volume, but water has more mass.
5. Atoms are the tiny pieces that make up matter.

## Apply Science Skills

**Science Reading Strategy: Facts and Examples** Read the instructions aloud, or call on a student to read them. Ask students, *What do you need to find?* Have students reread Mass on page 170. Tell students to find one fact about mass, and then an example. Have students complete their Fact and Example diagrams individually. Check answers as a class. The diagram might look like this:

### Mass

| Fact | Example |
|------|---------|
| Mass is a property that can be measured. | Use a balance to measure mass. |

**Using Visuals: Micrographs** Tell students, *You were able to see the atoms in sand (page 165) and nickel (page 175) using the micrographs in this lesson. The micrograph on page 177 shows you how the atoms of graphite look.* Read the instructions and questions aloud, or call on individual students to read them. Help students with new words. Then have pairs ask and answer the questions. Have them write their answers in their notebooks. Check answers and write them on the board.

**Answers**

1. Possible answers: Different: The graphite is shiny, but the graphite atoms are not. Same: A pencil lead is soft, and these atoms look soft. The photo and the micrograph are the same substance.
2. (Students point to six-sided crystals in the micrograph.)

## Discuss

Read the discussion questions aloud. Have students discuss the questions in pairs or in small groups. Then discuss them as a class. On poster paper, make a three-column list of students' responses, with the object name in column 1, whether it is measured in column 2, and how it is measured in column 3. Invite volunteers to draw small pictures of the objects.

Workbook pages 85–86 may now be assigned.

Workbook pages 85–86 may now be assigned.

## Evaluation

### Self-Assessment Questions

Write the following questions on the board and have students respond in their notebooks. Encourage them to share their responses in small groups or as a class.

1. How can finding facts and examples help me in reading?
2. How can micrographs help me understand new ideas?
3. What was difficult for me in this lesson?
4. What was easy for me in this lesson?
5. What was most enjoyable in this lesson?

# Lesson 2

# Before You Read, pages 178–181

Have students preview these pages individually or in pairs. Ask, *What will you learn in this lesson?*

## Vocabulary

Read the captions aloud, or call on individual students to read them. Help students understand and pronounce new words. Use pictures, props, and mime. Have students read the captions again silently.

Ask picture and comprehension questions for each item. Read the key words (page 179) aloud and have students say them after you. Then have students close their books. Point to the pictures and ask questions to elicit the key words.

### Practice

Read the instructions aloud. Elicit one or more definitions, if helpful. Have students define the words in pairs or small groups. Check answers by calling on individual students to read their sentences. Write the definitions on the board.

---

**Possible Answers**
- boiling point: the temperature at which a liquid changes to a gas; the boiling point of water is 100˚ Celsius (212˚ Fahrenheit)
- chemical change: change in chemicals in matter
- melting point: the temperature at which a solid melts; the melting point of water is 0˚ Celsius (32˚ Fahrenheit)
- physical change: change in appearance of matter, but it's still the same matter
- states: forms; the three states of matter are solid, liquid, and gas

---

 Workbook page 87 may now be assigned.

Workbook page 87 may now be assigned.

## Science Skills

**Science Reading Strategy: Idea Maps**  Write *Idea Maps* on the board. Tell students, *An idea map can help you understand and remember information.* Have students open their books to page 180. Read the heading, introduction, and text aloud, or call on individual students to read them.

Ask, *When do you draw an idea map? What does the map show? What does it help you do? What do you copy into your notebook? What's another name for an idea map?* (a word web) Draw the incomplete idea map on the board and have students copy it into their notebooks. Tell students, *You can add more circles if you need them.* Have students look back at page 169 and reread the page again silently. Then have them complete the idea map in pairs. When they have finished, elicit the information and write it on the board. The map might look like this:

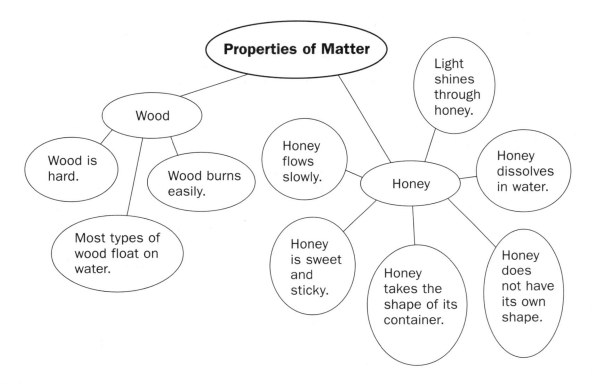

Workbook pages 88–89 may now be assigned.

**Using Visuals: States of Matter Illustrations**  Ask, *What are the three states of matter? Can you give an example of each state?* Have students look at page 178, if helpful. Tell students, *The illustrations on page 181 show the three states of matter, but not the way you and I see them. These illustrations show matter at the level of atoms.*

Have students read the heading at the top of page 181. Ask, *What visuals did you learn about in other lessons?* (diagrams, cycle diagrams, photographs, pie charts, sectional diagrams, photo sequences, illustrations, deep space photos, micrographs) *What visual will you practice using in this lesson?*

Read the introduction and captions aloud, or call on individual students to read them. Read the questions aloud. Help students with new words. Have students study the illustrations. Then have pairs ask and answer the questions. Have them write their answers in their notebooks. Check answers and write them on the board.

---

**Answers**
1. Atoms move the most as a gas because they are farther apart.
2. Atoms move the least as a solid because they are close together.
3. The atoms of a liquid move more than the atoms of a solid.

---

Workbook page 90 may now be assigned.

## Lesson ②

---

## States of Matter, pages 182–189
### Solids, page 182
### Liquids, page 183

---

### Preview Pages

Have students preview the pages and predict what they will learn.

### Teach Pages

Read the text and the captions aloud, or call on individual students to read them. Help students with new words. Elicit the key word (states), the sentence it is in, and the definition.

Have students read the pages again to themselves. Alternatively, have students read aloud to each other in pairs or small groups. Remind students to use the reading strategies they have learned in other units to help them understand. Have pairs of students ask each other questions about the reading. Follow up with your own comprehension and picture questions.

**Understand Information** Ask, *What's the science reading strategy in this lesson? What does an idea map help you connect? How does an idea map help you?* Say, *Let's make an idea map of the first paragraph on page 182.* Draw an oval on the board. Ask, *What's this paragraph about?* Write *States of Matter* in the oval. Ask, *What are the three states?* Elicit and write them on the board. Have students copy the idea map into their notebooks. Tell them to use a full page because they will add more information to it later. The map might look like this:

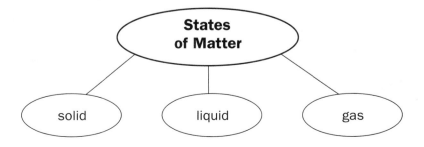

**Organize Information**  Depending on students' abilities, you may want to do the following activity as a class. Say, *Now let's add some more information to your idea map. Find more facts about solid and liquid matter on pages 182–183. Add them to your idea map.* The map might look like this:

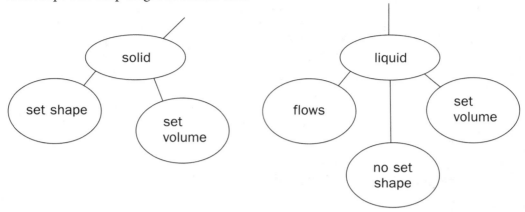

---

**Language Tip:** Multiple Meanings: *State*

Have students read the text in the Language Tip box. Ask, *What does* state *mean in this lesson?* (form) Write the definition on the board. Ask, *What is another meaning of state?* (area of land) Write the definition on the board. Say, *Some words have two or more different meanings.* Elicit other words students have learned that have multiple meanings. (space, matter)

---

**Science at Home:** Liquids, Shape, and Volume

Ask students to look at the title and picture and then predict what the text might be about. Read the text aloud, or call on a student to read it. Ask comprehension questions. Tell students to do this activity at home and report their observations the next day.

---

## Optional Activity

Bring to class five or six different containers (a plastic soda bottle, a tall and a short glass, a jar, and so on) and a container of five or six cups of water. Ask students to guess which container will make a cup of water look as if it has the highest volume and which will make it look as if it has the lowest volume. Pour one cup of water into each container. Ask students how the design of the containers makes the same volume look different.

Have pairs of students answer the first two questions. Have them write the questions and answers in their notebooks. Check answers before going on. Answer the third question together as a class.

**Answers**
1. The three different states of matter are solid, liquid, and gas.
2. Liquid matter does not have a set shape. Liquid matter does have a set volume.
3. Possible answers: A solid has a set shape, but a liquid doesn't. A liquid flows, but a solid doesn't.

## Gases, page 184
## Changing States of Matter, page 185

### Preview Pages

Have students preview the pages and predict what they will learn.

### Teach Pages

Read the text and the captions aloud, or call on individual students to read them. Help students with new words. Elicit the key word (states), the sentence it is in, and the definition.

Have students read the pages again to themselves. Alternatively, have students read aloud to each other in pairs or small groups. Remind students to use the reading strategies they have learned in other units to help them understand. Have pairs of students ask each other questions about the reading. Follow up with your own comprehension and picture questions.

**Understand Information** Ask, *What's the science reading strategy in this lesson? When do you make an idea map?* (after you read) *What information would you put in an idea map about gases? What information would you put in an idea map about changing states of matter?* Elicit ideas from students.

### As You Read: Idea Maps

Have students read the text in the As You Read box and copy the idea map into their notebooks. You may want them to add it to the idea map they made for solids and liquids. Have students complete the information about gases individually. Check answers as a class.

**Organize Information** Ask, *Can a solid change to a liquid? Can a liquid change to a gas? How does that happen? What are the atoms doing in each state of matter?* Have students draw pictures in their notebooks of the changes that are taking place as matter goes from solid to liquid and liquid to gas.

---

**Language Tip:** Contraction: *Do/Don't*

Read the text in the Language Tip box aloud, or have a volunteer read it to the class. Write *do not = don't* on the board. Have students write the line in their notebooks. Say, *This is a negative contraction.* Ask students to locate the sentences in the text that contain *do not* or *don't* and read them aloud. Ask, *How do you make negative contractions? What are some other negative contractions?* If students need more work on contractions, write full negatives on the board, elicit and write the contractions, and have students copy them into their notebooks and work on pronunciation. (doesn't, isn't, aren't, can't, didn't, wasn't, couldn't, won't)

---

**Environment Watch:** Melting Glaciers

Ask students to look at the title and the picture, and then predict what the text might be about. Ask, *What do you remember about glaciers from Unit 3?* Elicit information and write it in the form of an idea map on the board.

Read the text aloud, or call on a student to read it. Help students with new words. Ask comprehension questions. Have students make a sequence diagram about melting glaciers. If possible, find sequential photos of melting glaciers for the class to look at. Bring photos of the low-lying Maldives Islands in the Indian Ocean. Discuss with the class that scientists think these islands will disappear with rising oceans.

---

**Before You Go On**

Have pairs of students answer the first two questions. Have them write the questions and answers in their notebooks. Check answers before going on. Answer the third question together as a class.

**Answers**
1. No, gases don't have a set shape and volume.
2. The atoms in a solid are very close together.
3. Possible answers: liquid rock changing into solid rock; solid butter changing into liquid butter; boiling water changing into water vapor; and so on

---

## Changing States of Matter (continued), pages 186–187

### Preview Pages

Have students preview the pages and predict what they will learn.

**Teach Pages**

Read the text and captions aloud, or call on individual students to read them. Help students with new words. Elicit any key words (melting point, boiling point, state), the sentences they are in, and their definitions. Have students read the pages again to themselves. Alternatively, have students read aloud to each other in pairs or small groups. Remind students to use the reading strategies they have learned in other units to help them understand. Have pairs ask each other questions about the reading. Follow up with your own comprehension and picture questions.

**Understand Information**  Ask, *What is the reading strategy in this lesson? What are these pages about? What information would you put in an idea map about boiling and melting points?* Elicit ideas from students. Answer any questions.

**Organize Information**  Tell students, *Now let's make an idea map about the information on pages 186 and 187.* Start an idea map on the board, if needed. Have students work in pairs or in small groups to complete their maps. Ask volunteers to complete a map on the board. The map might look like this:

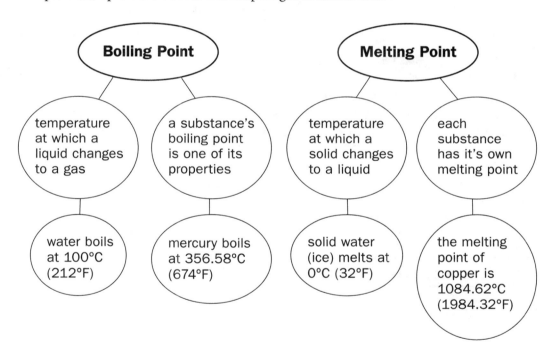

## REACHING ALL STUDENTS: Visual Learners

As a class, make a diagram showing water changing from a solid to a liquid to a gas at its melting point and boiling point. The diagram might look like this:

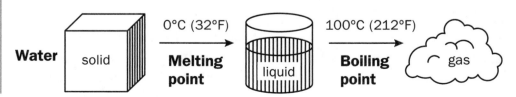

## Science Now: Steam Power

Ask students to look at the title and illustration to predict what the text might be about. Read the text aloud, or call on a student to read it. Help students with new words. Ask comprehension questions. Find pictures of hot springs and geysers in Iceland. Tell the class that Iceland is a country with a lot of hot springs. It uses steam and hot water for most of its energy needs—from making electricity to heating homes. Discuss with students the benefits of this kind of energy.

## Leaders in Science: Anders Celsius

Ask students to look at the title and illustration to predict what the text might be about. Ask, *Where have you heard the word* Celsius *before?* Read the text aloud, or call on a student to read it. Help students with new words.

Ask critical thinking questions such as, *Why did Celsius assign 0° and 100° to the melting and boiling points of water?* (Everyone knows and uses water, so this makes the scale easier to use.) *What other measurements are based on water?* (A liter of water is 1 kilogram. The density of a liter of water is 1.)

### Before You Go On

Have pairs of students answer the first two questions. Have them write the questions and answers in their notebooks. Check answers before going on. Answer the third question together as a class.

#### Answers
1. The boiling point of mercury is 356.58° Celsius (674° Fahrenheit).
2. Two properties of a substance are its boiling point and its melting point.
3. You need to store ice at a temperature below 0° Celsius (32° Fahrenheit), because ice will melt above 0° Celsius.

## Physical and Chemical Changes, pages 188–189

### Preview Pages

Have students preview the pages and predict what they will learn.

### Teach Pages

Read the text and the captions aloud, or call on individual students to read them. Help students with new words. Elicit any key words (physical change, chemical change, state), the sentences they are in, and their definitions.

Have students read the pages again to themselves. Alternatively, have pairs or small groups of students read aloud to each other. Remind students to use the reading strategies they have learned in other units to help them understand. Have pairs ask each other questions about the reading. Follow up with your own comprehension and picture questions.

**Understand Information** Ask, *What is the reading strategy in this lesson? What are these pages about? What information would you put in an idea map about physical and chemical changes?* Elicit ideas from students. Answer any questions.

**Organize Information** Ask students to reread pages 188 and 189. Tell students, *You're going to make an idea map of the examples of physical and chemical changes.* Make two circles on the board and write *Physical Changes* in one and *Chemical Changes* in the other. Have pairs of students make idea maps in their notebooks of two examples for each kind of change. Check answers as a class. Have volunteers complete the idea map on the board.

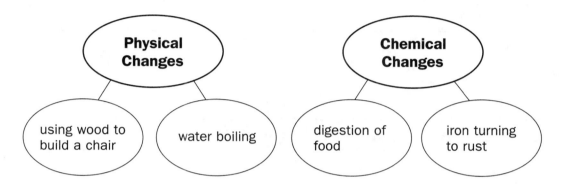

---

**Language Tip:** *Appear/Appearance*

Read the text in the Language Tip box aloud or have a volunteer read it to the class. Write *appear* ⟶ *verb* and *appearance* ⟶ *noun* on the board. Underline *ance* and say, *Nouns sometimes have the ending -ance.* Write the verb *disappear* on the board and elicit its meaning and its part of speech. Then ask students to guess the noun form. (disappearance) Write *disappearance* on the board, and have students copy the information on the board into their notebooks.

---

**HISTORY CONNECTION:** Stainless Steel

Ask students to look at the title and photograph to predict what the text might be about. Read the text aloud, or call on a student to read it. Help students with new words. Ask comprehension questions. Ask students if they can think of other things made of stainless steel. If possible, bring in pictures of other stainless steel items, such as eating utensils, cooking utensils, sinks, and so on. Ask, *Why do we use stainless steel for these things?*

Have pairs of students answer the first two questions. Have them write the questions and answers in their notebooks. Check answers before going on. Answer the third question together as a class.

**Answers**
1. The two main types of changes in matter are physical changes and chemical changes.
2. During a chemical change, the chemicals that make up the matter are changed and a different type of matter is formed.
3. Possible answers: Other examples of physical changes are melting or cooling metal, rock, or plastic; wood reformed to make things; paper and newspaper; and so on.

For more information, go to www.longmanusa.com/science for links to interesting websites about matter.

# Review and Practice, pages 190–191

## Vocabulary

If students need help in reviewing the vocabulary, see the Optional Vocabulary Activities (pages vii–viii). Have students complete the exercise individually. Check answers as a class.

**Answers**
1. states
2. melting point
3. physical change
4. boiling point
5. chemical change

## Check Your Understanding

Have students answer the questions individually, in pairs, or in small groups. If students need extra support, tell them to look at the information in their notebooks or allow students to look back at the text. Then have students share their answers with the class. Write the answers on the board.

**Answers**
1. Solids have a set shape and volume. Gases have no set shape or volume.
2. The atoms in a liquid flow. They do not have a set shape.
3. Possible answer: An example of a physical change is boiling water.
4. Possible answer: An example of a chemical change is rust.

## Apply Science Skills

**Science Reading Strategy: Idea Maps** Read the instructions aloud, or call on a student to read them. Have students look back at pages 188–189. Draw an idea map on the board and tell students they need to write facts about physical and chemical changes, not just give an example. Have students complete their maps individually or in pairs. Then elicit the information and write it on the board. The map might look like this:

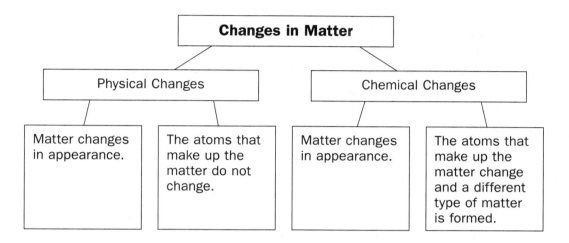

**Using Visuals: States of Matter Illustrations** Read the instructions aloud, or call on individual students to read them. Have students reread silently, if helpful. Ask comprehension questions to make sure students understand: *What does the line at the left show? What does the line at the bottom show? What is the melting point? What is the boiling point?*

Have students study the graph for a few moments. Then have pairs ask and answer the questions. Have them write their answers in their notebooks. Check answers as a class and write them on the board.

> **Answers**
> **1.** The atoms start to move more, move faster, and move apart. They don't have a set shape.
> **2.** The atoms move very quickly and move far apart.

## Discuss

Read the discussion question aloud. Have students discuss the question in small groups. Circulate to help and comment on students' responses. Allow time for students to share their answers with the class. Have students show the class things they have with them that were made by a substance changing state.

Workbook pages 91–92 may now be assigned.

### Self-Assessment Questions

Write the following questions on the board. Have students respond in their notebooks. Encourage them to share their responses in small groups or as a class.

1. How can making an idea map help me in reading?
2. How can states of matter illustrations help me understand information?
3. What was difficult for me in this lesson?
4. What was easy for me in this lesson?
5. What was most enjoyable in this lesson?

# Unit Review, pages 192–193

## Warm Up

Have pairs of students list the main ideas in Unit 5. Ask students to use the reading selection headings to group the main ideas. Alternatively, students may organize the main ideas in an idea map.

Ask pairs to exchange their completed list or idea map. Each pair should review their newly acquired list to see if any important information is missing. If information is missing, the pair should add it.

## Vocabulary

Have students answer the questions individually, with a partner, or in small groups, depending on how much support they need. Check answers as a class as you write the correct answers on the board.

---

**Answers**
1. You can measure volume with a container.
2. You can measure mass with a balance.
3. You have to weigh something to find its mass.
4. Matter is anything that has mass and takes up space.
5. Atoms are the tiny pieces that make up matter.
6. Density is the mass of something per unit of volume.
7. A physical change happens when matter changes state.
8. A chemical change happens to food when you eat it.
9. Another word for the three forms matter can have is *states*.
10. A substance changes from a solid to a liquid at its melting point.
11. A substance changes from a liquid to a gas at its melting point.

---

## Check Your Understanding

Have students work individually, with a partner, or in small groups, depending on how much support they need. Check answers as a class as you write the correct answers on the board.

**Answers**
1. False. Salt is a pure substance.
2. True
3. False. Ice melting is an example of a physical change.
4. False. Liquids have no set shape.
5. False. Physical properties can be used to tell substances apart.

## Extension Project

Read the instructions aloud, or call on a student to read them. Have students make their charts of solids, liquids, and gases in pairs or in small groups. After students have finished, have them make a master chart to hang in the classroom. Encourage students to look for picture examples to place next to the names.

## Apply Science Skills

**Using Visuals: States of Matter Illustrations** Read the instructions aloud, or call on a student to read them. Give students a few minutes to study the illustration. Elicit two sentences about the part of the picture labeled 1 (a gas). Then have students work individually or in pairs to complete the exercise. Check answers as a class.

**Answers**
1. The temperature is higher than 100°C. Water is a gas. It has no set shape or volume. The atoms are moving very fast.
2. The temperature is higher than 1°C. Water is a liquid. It has a set volume but no set shape. The atoms are moving around.
3. The temperature is lower than 0°C. Water is a solid. It has a set shape and volume. The atoms are not moving around.

## Read More About It

Bring at least one of the suggested books to class. Show the cover and some of the inside pages to students as a preview. Ask students to predict what the book is about. Read an excerpt aloud to the class. Then ask several comprehension questions. Read the excerpt again before calling on students to answer. Encourage students to find this or another suggested book in their school library or local bookstore.

Workbook pages 93–94 may now be assigned.

## Unit Experiment, pages 194–195
### Can You Observe Density?

### Preview

Call on a student to read the experiment question aloud. Have students predict what they might be doing. Read aloud the introduction, purpose, and materials, or have individual students read them. Help students with new words. Make sure students understand the experiment.

### Do the Experiment

For this experiment, you'll need to bring to class one or more of the items pictured. Ideally, students perform this experiment in medium-sized groups. If you have more limited resources, you could do the experiment as a class.

Read each of the What to Do instructions aloud, or have a student read them. Ask comprehension questions to make sure students know what to do. Have students perform the tasks. Discuss the conclusions and answer the questions as a class.

Workbook page 95 may now be assigned for students to use in writing up and drawing conclusions about the experiment. Workbook page 96 may then be assigned.

# Unit 6 Sound and Light

## Unit Overview

| Lesson | Content | Science Skills | | Experiment |
|--------|---------|----------------|---|------------|
| | | Reading Strategies | Using Visuals | |
| 1 | • Sound: Sound Waves, Echoes, Pitch and Frequency, Volume, Sound and Matter | Act It Out | Charts | How Does Light Reflect and Refract? |
| 2 | • Light: Reflection, Transparency, Colors of Light, Colors of Objects, Refraction, Prisms and Rainbows | Draw a Picture | Wave Diagrams | |

## Objectives

### Vocabulary
• Develop new vocabulary related to sound and light
• Use newly acquired vocabulary in context

### Concepts
• Learn about sound waves and their qualities
• Learn about electromagnetic waves
• Learn about visible light waves and their qualities

### Reading Strategies
• Act out a text to understand and remember information
• Draw a picture to understand and remember information
• Practice previously learned strategies

### Using Visuals
• Understand how to study charts for information
• Understand how to study wave diagrams for information

### Experiment
• Observe the reflection and refraction of light

## Unit Opener, pages 196–197

### Preview Topic

Ask students to preview these pages. Then ask, *What is this unit about? What is sound? What is light? What do you think you'll learn about sound and light?* Ask students what they see in the pictures. Encourage them to say whatever they can. Point to each picture and give a little more information about it.

### Unit Concepts

Read aloud the list of unit concepts for Lessons 1 and 2. Ask, *What words and sentences do you understand?* Elicit information about them. Tell students that they will learn the other information as they read the lessons.

### Get Ready

Read the instructions aloud, acting out (people talking, a bell ringing, soft, loud) where needed. Let students reread silently, if helpful. Have students copy the chart into their notebooks. Have students listen to sounds from inside the classroom or go to different locations in and around the school. When students have finished, make a master chart on the board and elicit information. Compare the volume of different sounds. Can the same sound be loud or soft? Which ones?

## Lesson ❶

## Before You Read, pages 198–201

Have students preview these pages individually or in pairs. Ask, *What will you learn in this lesson?*

### Vocabulary

Read the captions aloud, or call on students to read them. Help students understand and pronounce new words. Use pictures, props, and mime. Have students read the captions again silently. Ask picture and comprehension questions for each item. Read the key words (page 199) aloud again and have students say them after you. Then have them close their books. Point to the pictures and ask questions to elicit the key words.

### Practice

Have students write the sentences in their notebooks. Then have them choose the correct answers and write them in the sentences. Check answers by calling on individual students. Write the letters of the correct answers on the board.

| **Answers** | | |
|---|---|---|
| **1.** a. pitch | **3.** a. frequency | **5.** a. vibrations |
| **2.** b. echo | **4.** c. Volume | **6.** c. sound waves |

Workbook page 97 may now be assigned.

## Science Skills

**Science Reading Strategy: Act It Out** Have students open their books to page 200. Read the heading and the introduction aloud, or call on individual students to read them aloud. Write *Act it out* on the board and elicit the meaning. (Use your body and objects around you to help students understand and remember.)

Read the caption and have students act it out. Let them feel the vibrations of their vocal cords. Then read or have students read paragraph by paragraph. Help students understand new words. Let students reread each paragraph, then say, *Act it out.* Model acting out the first paragraph, if needed.

Workbook page 98 may now be assigned.

**Using Visuals: Charts** Have students read the heading at the top of page 201. Ask, *What visuals did you learn about in other units?* (diagrams, cycle diagrams, photographs, pie charts, sectional diagrams, photo sequences, illustrations, deep space photos, micrographs, states of matter illustrations) Ask, *What visual will you practice using in this lesson?*

Have students look at the chart. Say, *This is a science chart. Charts give us information.* Ask, *Do you see pictures in the chart?* (no) Ask, *What do you see?* (words and numbers) Say, *Charts give us information in words and numbers. Charts usually compare different pieces of information.*

Read the introduction, captions, and questions aloud, or call on individual students to read them. Have students reread silently. Ask questions to check understanding and elicit meanings of vocabulary. Have students study the chart for a few minutes. Then have pairs ask and answer the questions. Have them write their answers in their notebooks. Check answers and write them on the board.

---

**Answers**
1. The softest sound is breathing. The loudest sound is a plane taking off.
2. Rain is louder than a mosquito.
3. A plane taking off is 50 decibels louder than a motorcycle.

---

Workbook pages 99–100 may now be assigned.

## Lesson ❶

# Sound, pages 202–203

## Preview Pages

Have students preview these pages and predict the topic. Ask, *What are you going to learn on these pages? What do you already know about sound?*

## Teach Pages

Read the text and the captions aloud, or call on individual students to read them. Help students with new words. Elicit the key word (vibration), the sentences it is in, and the definition.

Have students read the pages again to themselves. Alternatively, have students read aloud to each other in pairs or small groups. Remind students to use the reading strategies they have learned in other units to help them understand. Have pairs of students ask each other questions about the reading. Follow up with your own comprehension and picture questions.

**Understand Information** Bring to class a drumstick and a drum, preferably one with a surface that vibrates visibly. Alternatively, bring cymbals or a tuning fork. Ask students to observe carefully while you hit the drum, cymbal, or tuning fork.

Ask, *Did you see a vibration when I hit the (drum)? Did you hear a sound?* Say, *I'm going to hit the (drum) again, but I want you to cover your ears this time.* Hit the (drum) a few times, have students uncover their ears, and ask, *Did you hear the (drum) clearly?* (no) *Why not?* (The vibrations didn't reach the eardrums well.)

**Organize Information** Have students make a Main Idea and Details chart for the last paragraph on page 203. If helpful, elicit the main idea. The chart might look like this:

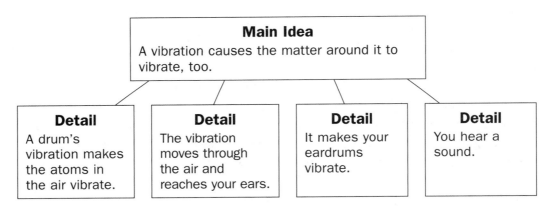

**Main Idea**
A vibration causes the matter around it to vibrate, too.

**Detail**
A drum's vibration makes the atoms in the air vibrate.

**Detail**
The vibration moves through the air and reaches your ears.

**Detail**
It makes your eardrums vibrate.

**Detail**
You hear a sound.

**Language Tip:** *Vibrate/Vibration*

Have students read the text in the Language Tip box. Write *vibrate* and *vibration* on the board and have students write the words in their notebooks. Say, *Find sentences on page 203 with the word* vibrate. (It vibrates, or moves up and down. This tuning fork is vibrating.) Ask, *Is* vibrate *a noun or a verb?* (a verb) Write *verb* next to *vibrate* and have students copy it into their notebooks.

Say, *Find sentences on page 203 with the word* vibration. (This vibration makes a sound. A vibration causes the matter around it to vibrate, too.) Ask, *What part of speech is* vibration? (a noun) Write *noun* on the board next to *vibration*. Ask, *What are other examples of verb and noun pairs ending in* -ate *and* -tion? Elicit examples from previous units and write them on the board. (pollinate/pollination; germinate/germination; communicate/communication; illustrate/illustration) Have students write them in their notebooks.

Have pairs of students answer the first two questions. Have them write the questions and answers in their notebooks. Check answers before going on. Answer the third question together as a class.

**Answers**
1. Vibrations make sounds.
2. The eardrum catches vibrations.
3. Possible answers: Loud noises make us look around. Hearing sounds alerts us to danger.

## Sound Waves, page 204
## Echoes, page 205

### Preview Pages

Have students preview the pages and predict what they will learn.

### Teach Pages

Read the text and the captions aloud, or call on individual students to read them. Help students with new words. Elicit any key words (vibrations, sound waves, echo), the sentences they are in, and their definitions.

Have students read the pages again to themselves. Alternatively, have pairs or small groups of students read aloud to each other. Remind students to use the reading strategies they have learned in other units to help them understand. Have the pairs ask each other questions about the reading. Follow up with your own comprehension and picture questions.

**Understand Information** Have individual students draw a picture about sound waves. Suggest a picture similar to the photographs on page 204. Call on a few students to explain their drawings to the class. Alternatively, have students draw diagrams that show the information about echoes.

### REACHING ALL STUDENTS: Kinesthetic Learners

Take students outside to act out the information about sound waves and echoes. If possible, show students the ripples that are formed when you throw a rock into water. Look for locations where students can make echoes.

**Organize Information** Have students make an idea map of the information. Begin by writing *Sound Waves* in a circle on the board. Have students complete the idea map individually, in pairs, or in small groups. Circulate to check progress. Check information as a class by having volunteers complete the idea map on the board. The map might look like this:

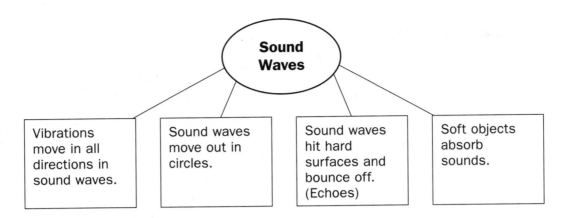

Sound
Waves

| Vibrations move in all directions in sound waves. | Sound waves move out in circles. | Sound waves hit hard surfaces and bounce off. (Echoes) | Soft objects absorb sounds. |

## Poetry Connection: Basho

Ask students to look at the title and photograph to predict what the text might be about. Ask, *What do you see in the photo? What's the frog doing? Can you imagine this sound?*

Read the text aloud, or call on a student to read it. Help students with new words. Ask comprehension questions. Read the poem again. Ask students to visualize the poem. Ask, *What did you see? Did you imagine a sound?* Say, *Try to make this sound.*

Have students copy the poem into their notebooks. Bring in a few other simple haiku poems by Basho. Many websites are devoted to Basho's poems.

## Science at Home: Making Echoes

Ask students to look at the title and predict what the text might be about. Read the text aloud, or call on a student to read it. Ask comprehension questions. Tell students to act out making echoes at home. Tell them to write their observations in their notebooks. Check their work in class the next day. Be sure to elicit why the sounds were different.

## Before You Go On

Have pairs of students answer the first two questions. Have them write the questions and answers in their notebooks. Check answers before going on. Answer the third question together as a class.

### Answers
1. Sound waves move out in circles in all directions.
2. You can hear echoes in places that have hard surfaces.
3. Possible answers: The gym/the cafeteria/the hallway is a good place to hear an echo.

## Pitch and Frequency, page 206

**Preview Page**

Have students preview the page and predict what they will learn.

**Teach Page**

Read the text and the captions aloud, or call on individual students to read them. Help students with new words. Elicit any key words (pitch, frequency, sound waves), the sentences they are in, and their definitions.

Have students read the page again to themselves. Alternatively, have students read aloud to each other in pairs or small groups. Remind students to use the reading strategies they have learned in other units to help them understand. Have pairs ask each other questions about the reading. Follow up with your own comprehension and picture questions.

---

**Language Tip:** *Frequent/Frequency*

Have students read the text in the Language Tip box. Write *frequent* and *frequency* on the board. Ask, *What does* frequent *mean?* Write the definition on the board. Write some examples of its use, such as *frequent flyer* and *frequent visitor*. Ask for example sentences. Point to the frequency diagrams. Ask, *Which waves are closer together, high-frequency waves or low-frequency waves? Which are not close together?* Have students copy the information on the board into their notebooks.

---

**Understand Information**  Say, *Let's act out high-pitch sounds. Put your finger to your throat. Make a high-pitch sound with your vocal cords.* Model the activity. *Now let's make a sound with a deep, low pitch.* Ask, *Can you feel the difference? Let's make each sound one more time.* Ask, *How did your throat vibrate for the high-pitch sound? How did it vibrate for the low-pitch sound? Which made it move quickly? Which made the air move slowly? Which pitch made low-frequency sound waves? Which pitch made high-frequency sounds?*

**Organize Information**  Have students make a T-chart to contrast high and low pitch, using the information on page 206. The chart might look like this:

| Pitch and Frequency | |
|---|---|
| **High pitch** | **Low pitch** |
| Air vibrates quickly | Air vibrates slowly |
| Sound waves are closer together | Sound waves are farther apart |
| High-frequency wave | Low-frequency wave |

# Exploring, page 207

## Preview Page

Have students preview the page and predict what they will learn.

## Teach Page

Read the text aloud, or call on individual students to read it. Help students with new words. Elicit any key words (frequency, sound waves, pitch), the sentence they are in, and their definitions.

Have students read the page again to themselves. Alternatively, have pairs or small groups of students read aloud to each other. Remind students to use the reading strategies they have learned in other units to help them understand. Have pairs of students ask each other questions about the reading. Follow up with your own comprehension and picture questions.

**Understand Information** Ask critical-thinking questions or put them on the board and have students discuss them in pairs or in small groups. For example, *Which two animals on this page can hear the lowest frequency sounds?* (elephants, humans) *Which can hear the highest?* (mice, cats) *Can we hear all the sounds elephants can hear?* (probably not) *Why do animals have different hearing adaptations?* (It helps them survive.)

**Organize Information** Work with students to make a chart of the animals on this page and their range of hearing frequencies.

## Optional Activity

Help students find different animal sounds on the Internet. Have students listen and then discuss the pitch and frequency of the sounds. Ask students how they say the different animal sounds in their native languages, and then teach the English version and spelling. Interesting animals might include cats (meow), mice (squeak), birds (tweet), roosters (cock-a-doodle-doo), dogs (woof, bowwow), cows (moo), sheep (baa).

### Before You Go On

Have pairs of students answer the first two questions. Have them write the questions and answers in their notebooks. Check answers before going on. Answer the third question together as a class.

#### Answers
1. Pitch is caused by the frequency of sound waves.
2. Low-frequency sound waves are far apart.
3. No, because some sounds mice make are too high-pitched.

## Volume, page 208
## Sound and Matter, page 209

**Preview Pages**

Have students preview the pages and predict what they will learn.

**Teach Pages**

Read the text aloud, or call on individual students to read it. Help students with new words. Elicit any key words (volume, sound waves, vibration), the sentences they are in, and their definitions.

Have students read the pages again to themselves. Alternatively, have pairs or small groups of students read aloud to each other. Remind students to use the reading strategies they have learned in other units to help them understand. Have pairs of students ask each other questions about the reading. Follow up with your own comprehension and picture questions.

**Understand Information** Have students take another look at the chart at the bottom of page 208. Compare this chart with the one on page 201. Ask, *How are the charts the same? How are they different?*

**Organize Information** Have students make a chart listing how sound waves travel through different types of matter using information on page 209. The chart might look like this:

| Sound Waves and Matter | | |
| --- | --- | --- |
| **Solids** | **Liquids** | **Gases** |
| Sound waves move most quickly through solids. | Sound moves more slowly through liquids. | Sound moves slowest through gases because the atoms are even farther apart. |
| The atoms in solids are close together. | The atoms are farther apart. | |
| The vibration can move quickly from atom to atom. | It takes longer for the vibration to reach each atom. | It takes a lot of time for the vibration to move from atom to atom. |

**As You Read:** Act It Out

Have students read the text in the As You Read box. Ask, *As you read, what should you do?* (act it out) Have students read the first paragraph on page 208 again to themselves. Have them act out tapping their fingers on the desk, first gently and quietly, then stronger and louder. Ask students if they can feel the difference in the amount of energy they are using.

**Language Tip:** Multiple Meanings: *Volume*

Have students read the text in the Language Tip box. Write *volume* on the board. Ask, *What did* volume *mean in the lesson on matter?* Write the definition on the board. Ask, *What does* volume *mean in this lesson on sound?* Write the definition on the board. Have students copy the information into their notebooks. Ask for additional example sentences for each meaning of *volume*.

### Before You Go On

Have pairs of students answer the first two questions. Have them write the questions and answers in their notebooks. Check answers before going on. Answer the third question together as a class. Have students go back to Unit 4 to check on the atmosphere of Venus.

**Answers**
1. Loud sounds have more energy.
2. Sound moves fastest through solids because the atoms are close together.
3. No, because there are thick clouds of poisonous gas on Venus.

For more information, go to www.longmanusa.com/science for links to interesting websites about sound and light.

## Review and Practice, pages 210–211

### Vocabulary

If students need help in reviewing the vocabulary, see the Optional Vocabulary Activities (pages vii–viii). Have students complete the exercise individually. Check answers as a class.

**Answers**
1. echo
2. Vibrations
3. frequency
4. volume
5. pitch
6. sound waves

### Check Your Understanding

Have students answer the questions individually, in pairs, or in small groups. If students need extra support, tell them to look at the information in their notebooks or allow students to look back at the text. Then have students share their answers with the class. Write the answers on the board.

**Answers**
1. People hear sounds when sound waves bounce off a hard surface.
2. Sound waves move out (in circles) in all directions.
3. Loud sounds have higher volume.
4. Sound travels fastest through solids.

## Apply Science Skills

**Science Reading Strategy: Act It Out** Read the instructions aloud, or call on a student to read them. Ask students, *What do you need to get?* Have students get a pen, ruler, or other hard object. Ask, *What do you do with it? What do you do next?*

Have students reread and act it out in pairs. Check by eliciting students' observations and writing them on the board. Ask students why the taps sounded different. (The taps sound different because sound travels more quickly through a solid than through the air. That gives the sound a different quality.)

**Using Visuals: Charts** Tell students, *You learned a lot using the charts in this lesson. This chart will show you some new information.* Read the instructions and questions aloud, or call on individual students to read them. Help students with new words. Review large numbers with the class, if needed. Have students study the chart for a few minutes. Then have pairs of students ask and answer the questions. Have them write their answers in their notebooks. Then elicit the correct answers and write them on the board.

> **Answers**
> 1. Sound travels 343 meters (1,125 feet) per second in air.
> 2. Sound travels faster in glass.
> 3. The sound travels faster in the steel strings of a guitar because sound travels faster in steel than in wood.

## Discuss

Read the discussion questions aloud. Write *pitch* and *volume* on the board and remind students to include these words in their discussions. Have students discuss the questions in pairs or small groups. Then discuss the questions as a class. Make a list of students' favorite instruments.

Workbook pages 101–102 may now be assigned.

## Evaluation

### Self-Assessment Questions

Write the following questions on the board and have students respond in their notebooks. Encourage students to share their responses in small groups or as a class.
1. How can acting it out help me in reading?
2. How can charts help me understand new ideas?
3. What was difficult for me in this lesson?
4. What was easy for me in this lesson?
5. What was most enjoyable in this lesson?

# Lesson ❷

## Before You Read, pages 212–215

Have students preview these pages individually or in pairs. Ask, *What will you learn in this lesson?*

### Vocabulary

Read the captions aloud, or call on students to read them. Help students understand and pronounce new words. Use pictures, props, and mime. Have students read the captions again silently. Ask picture and comprehension questions for each item. Read the key words (page 213) aloud and have students say them after you. Then have them close their books. Point to the pictures and ask questions to elicit the key words.

### Practice

Read the instructions aloud. Elicit one or more definitions, if helpful. Have students define the words in pairs or in small groups. Check by calling on individual students to read their sentences. Write the definitions on the board.

---

**Possible Answers**
- electromagnetic wave: it has its own energy; light is a type of this wave
- opaque: we can't see through it; light can't travel through it
- reflection: light waves bouncing off a surface
- refraction: when light hits transparent matter at an angle, it changes direction and bends
- transparent: we can see through it; light can travel through it
- translucent: light can travel through it; we can't see clearly through it

---

 Workbook page 103 may now be assigned.

### Science Skills

 **Science Reading Strategy: Draw a Picture** Tell students, *Drawing pictures can help you understand information.* Have students open their books to page 214. Read the heading, introduction, and text aloud, or call on individual students to read them. Help students with new words. Tell students to reread the paragraph again silently and look at the drawing.

Ask, *What happens when light hits a surface? Do all the waves bounce off the same way? What's an example of a smooth surface? How does light bounce off a smooth surface when it hits at an angle? Does the picture help you understand the underlined sentence in the first paragraph?*

Point out the second underlined sentence in the text. Read it aloud. Individually or in pairs, have students draw a picture to represent the second underlined sentence. Have students share their pictures as a class. Talk about the differences between the picture on page 214 and the pictures that students drew.

Workbook pages 104–105 may now be assigned.

**Using Visuals: Wave Diagrams** Have students look back at page 206. Hold up your book and point to the diagrams of the sound waves. Say, *These are diagrams of sound waves. In this lesson we'll study light waves. Light waves have frequency, too. We can show light waves like this. We can also show light waves as arrows.*

Have students read the heading at the top of page 215. Read the introduction and the captions aloud, or call on individual students to read them. Point out that we use the word *violet* instead of *purple* when talking about light. Have students reread silently. Ask questions to check understanding, such as (pointing to wavelength diagram), *What does this diagram define?* (pointing to the visible light diagram) *What does this diagram show? What does* visible *mean? What does each color of light have?*

Have students study the diagrams for a few minutes. Then have pairs ask and answer the questions. Have them write their answers in their notebooks. Check answers and write them on the board. Make sure students understand wavelength and how it relates to frequency.

> **Answers**
> **1.** Violet has the shortest wavelength.
> **2.** Red has the longest wavelength.
> **3.** Short wavelengths have high frequencies. Long wavelengths have low frequencies.

Workbook page 106 may now be assigned.

## Lesson ❷

# Light, pages 216–217

### Preview Pages

Have students preview the pages and predict what they will learn.

### Teach Pages

Read the text and the captions aloud, or call on individual students to read them. Help students with new words. Elicit the key word (electromagnetic waves), the sentences it is in, and the definition.

Have students read the pages again to themselves. Alternatively, have students read aloud to each other in pairs or small groups. Remind students to use the reading strategies they have learned in other units to help them understand. Have pairs ask each other questions about the reading. Follow up with your own comprehension and picture questions.

**Understand Information** Have students look at the diagram. Ask, *What kind of visual is this?* (a wave diagram) Say, *Study the diagram a few minutes, and then talk about it in* *pairs.* Write questions about the diagram on the board, such as, *Which electromagnetic waves have the longest wavelength? Which have the shortest wavelength? Which have higher frequencies, microwaves or infrared waves? Which has a longer wavelength, visible light or ultraviolet waves?* Have students ask and answer these questions in pairs or in small groups. Then elicit the correct answers and write them on the board.

**Organize Information** Say, *Let's draw a picture of the waves we can see and the waves we can't see. That will help us understand the electromagnetic spectrum, wavelength, and frequency.* Draw an eye in profile on the board. Then draw a vertical line with arrows at each end. Label the top of the line *Short wavelength, high frequency.* Label the bottom *Long wavelength, low frequency.* (See the final diagram below.) Ask, *What's the electromagnetic wave we can see?* (visible light) Write *Visible light* opposite the eye with an arrow pointing straight to the eye. Ask, *Can we see ultraviolet waves? Why not?* (the frequency is too high, the wavelength is too short) Write *Ultraviolet rays* above *Visible light,* and draw a straight arrow extending above the eye. Ask, *Can we see infrared waves? Why not?* (the frequency is too low, the wavelength is too long) Write *Infrared rays* below *Visible light,* and draw a straight arrow extending below the eye. Say, *Now draw the other electromagnetic waves on your picture diagram.*

Have students work in pairs to complete their diagrams. When they have finished, elicit information for the rest of the waves and show them on the board. Finally, have students add information about the use of each wave, or what it can do. The diagram might look like this:

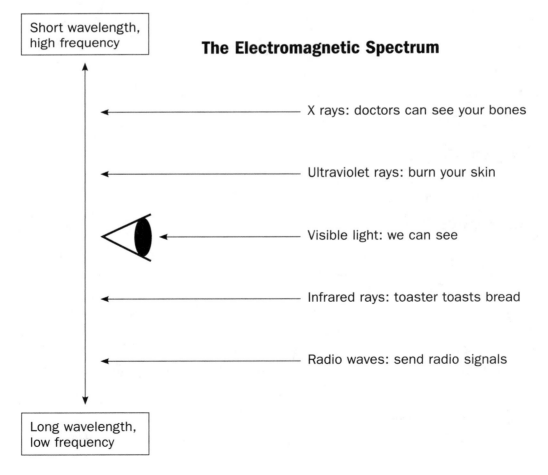

**The Electromagnetic Spectrum**

Short wavelength, high frequency

X rays: doctors can see your bones

Ultraviolet rays: burn your skin

Visible light: we can see

Infrared rays: toaster toasts bread

Radio waves: send radio signals

Long wavelength, low frequency

## Language Tip: Possessive Adjectives

Have students read the text in the Language Tip box. Ask, *What kinds of words are in the left column?* (personal pronouns) *What kinds of words are in the right column?* (possessive adjectives) Review the use of possessive adjectives, stressing that they are always paired with a noun. Give examples: *my book, your pen.* Have students look for the sentences on page 216 that contain possessive adjectives.

## Environment Watch: UV Rays

Ask students to look at the title and predict what the text might be about. Read the text aloud, or call on a student to read it. Ask comprehension questions. Then ask, *What do we wear to protect ourselves from ultraviolet rays?* (a hat, sunscreen, sunglasses) *What could happen if we don't protect ourselves?* (sunburn, skin cancer) If possible, look for current articles about the loss of the ozone layer to read and discuss with the class.

## Optional Activity

Write on the board, *How long does it take sunlight to reach the earth?* Have students look back at the distance chart on page 161. Ask, *How far is it from the sun to the earth?* (150,000,000 kilometers) Write the distance on the board. Ask, *How fast does light travel?* (300,000 meters per second) Write the speed on the board and add *1,000 meters = 1 kilometer.* Ask, *How many kilometers is 300,000 meters?* (300 kilometers) If students are fairly capable in math, let them find the answer in pairs or small groups. If not, guide them in doing the math to reach 500,000 seconds, then divide by minutes (60 seconds) and hours (60 minutes) to arrive at 139 hours. It takes sunlight 139 hours to reach the earth.

### Before You Go On

Have pairs of students answer the first two questions. Have them write the questions and answers in their notebooks. Check answers before going on. Answer the third question together as a class.

**Answers**
1. Electromagnetic waves are different from sound waves because they have their own electrical and magnetic energy. They can travel through space.
2. We can see visible light waves.
3. Possible answers: Ultraviolet waves and infrared rays can be dangerous.

## Reflection, page 218
## Transparency, page 219

Reflection, page 218
Transparency, page 219

### Preview Pages

Have students preview the pages and predict what they will learn.

### Teach Pages

Read the text aloud, or call on individual students to read it. Help students with new words. Elicit any key words (reflection, transparent, opaque, translucent), the sentences they are in, and their definitions.

Have students read the pages again to themselves. Alternatively, have students read aloud to each other in pairs or small groups. Remind students to use the reading strategies they have learned in other units to help them understand. In pairs, have students ask each other questions about the reading. Follow up with your own comprehension and picture questions.

**Understand Information** Ask, *What's the science reading strategy in this lesson?* Say, *A picture will help us understand transparent, opaque, and translucent. What's a material that's transparent?* (clear glass) Draw a transparent cube on the board and label it. Ask, *What's a translucent material I can draw as a cube?* (frosted glass) Draw it and label it. Ask, *What's an opaque material I can draw as a cube?* (wood, metal, and so on) Draw one on the board and label it. Have students copy the cubes into their notebooks. Say, *Let's reread the section about transparent matter.* Then ask a volunteer to draw arrows on the board showing how light waves would travel through transparent material. In pairs or in small groups, have students complete their drawings with light waves moving through translucent and opaque materials. The drawings might look like this:

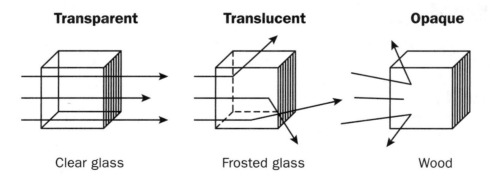

| Transparent | Translucent | Opaque |
| --- | --- | --- |
| Clear glass | Frosted glass | Wood |

**Organize Information** Have students make a Cause-and-Effect diagram about smooth surfaces using the information on page 218. Then have them make another one about uneven surfaces. The diagrams might look like this:

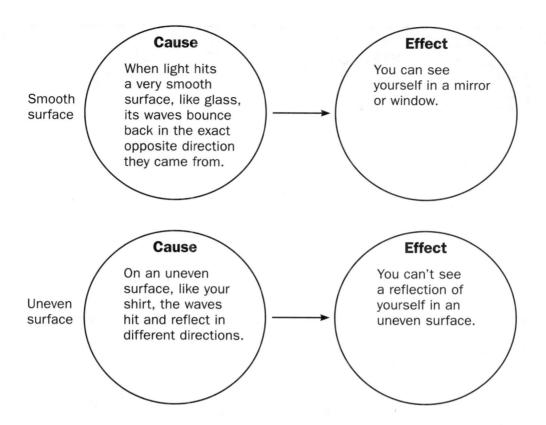

**Cause**
Smooth surface

When light hits a very smooth surface, like glass, its waves bounce back in the exact opposite direction they came from.

**Effect**

You can see yourself in a mirror or window.

**Cause**
Uneven surface

On an uneven surface, like your shirt, the waves hit and reflect in different directions.

**Effect**

You can't see a reflection of yourself in an uneven surface.

## Science at Home: Mirrors

Ask students to look at the title and the picture, and then predict what the text might be about. Read the text aloud, or call on a student to read it. Ask comprehension questions. Tell students to look around today at the mirrors they see and write down the places they see them. Check their results in the next class.

## Language Tip: *Material*

Have students read the text in the Language Tip box. Review the definition of *matter* and *properties*. Say, *Transparent, translucent, and opaque are properties.*

## Before You Go On

Have pairs of students answer the first two questions. Have them write the questions and answers in their notebooks. Check answers before going on. Answer the third question together as a class.

**Answers**
1. Reflection allows you to see most objects.
2. Possible answers: Glass, clear water, and clean air are transparent. Wood, metal, walls, a door, and a floor are opaque. Frosted glass is translucent.
3. Possible answer: A mirror reflects the light back at us. With plain glass, most of the light passes through. Very little is reflected back.

## Colors of Light, page 220
## Colors of Objects, page 221

Colors of Light, page 220
Colors of Objects, page 221

**Preview Pages**

Have students preview the pages and predict what they will learn.

**Teach Pages**

Read the text and the captions aloud, or call on individual students to read them. Help students with new words. Elicit any key words or related words (reflect, reflected), the sentences they are in, and their definitions. Have students read the pages again to themselves. Alternatively, have students read aloud to each other in pairs or small groups. Remind students to use the reading strategies they have learned in other units to help them understand. Have pairs ask each other questions about the reading. Follow up with your own comprehension and picture questions.

**Understand Information** Point to different objects in the room. Have students tell you which color each object is reflecting and which colors are being absorbed.

---

**Language Tip:** Compound Words: *wavelength*

Read the text in the Language Tip box aloud or have a volunteer read it to the class. Write *wave + length = wavelength*. Say, *This word is made of two shorter words.* Elicit the meanings of *wave* and *length*. Explain that sometimes we can put two words together to make a new word, called a compound word. Elicit or teach some other examples of compound words. (sunlight, notebook, keyboard, bathroom, somebody, haircut, anything) Have students create sentences using the compound words.

---

**Organize Information** Pointing to the paragraph on page 220, tell students, *Now you'll make a Main Idea and Details chart for the paragraph on page 220.* The chart might look like this:

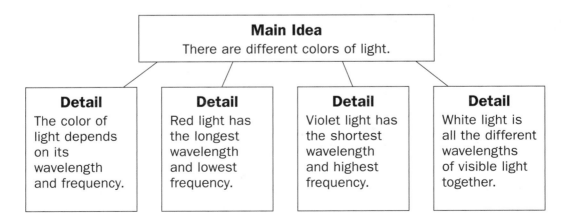

| **Main Idea** |
| There are different colors of light. |

| **Detail** | **Detail** | **Detail** | **Detail** |
|---|---|---|---|
| The color of light depends on its wavelength and frequency. | Red light has the longest wavelength and lowest frequency. | Violet light has the shortest wavelength and highest frequency. | White light is all the different wavelengths of visible light together. |

## As You Read: Draw a Picture

Have students read the text in the As You Read box. Ask, *What should you do? What are the different wavelengths of light?* Have students reread the second paragraph on page 221. If needed, draw a simple apple on the board. Elicit the name of one color the apple absorbs. Then draw a light ray being absorbed by the apple and label it. Have students complete their drawings in pairs or individually.

## Science Now: Lasers

Ask students to look at the title and the photograph to predict what the text might be about. Read the text aloud, or call on a student to read it. Help students with new words. Ask comprehension questions. Ask students if they know of any other uses of lasers. (Doctors use lasers for cutting and burning. Some guns have lasers. Lasers are used as pointers.)

## Before You Go On

Have pairs of students answer the first two questions. Have them write the questions and answers in their notebooks. Check answers before going on. Answer the third question together as a class.

### Answers
1. White light is all the different wavelengths of light together.
2. The different colors of light are red, orange, yellow, green, blue, and violet.
3. A lemon absorbs red, orange, green, blue, and violet wavelengths.

## Refraction, page 222
## Prisms and Rainbows, page 223

### Preview Pages

Have students preview the pages and predict what they will learn.

### Teach Pages

Read the text and captions aloud, or call on individual students to read them. Help students with new words. Elicit the key word (refraction), the sentence it is in, and the definition.

Have students read the pages again to themselves. Alternatively, have pairs or small groups of students read aloud to each other. Remind students to use the reading strategies they have learned in other units to help them understand. Have students ask each other questions about the reading in pairs. Follow up with your own comprehension and picture questions.

**Understand Information** Say, *A picture can help you understand information. It can also help you remember it better. Let's draw a picture of how a prism separates white light into its different colors.* Let students look back at the picture on page 220. Say, *Draw a picture of the prism, white light, and different colors of light in your notebook. Instead of using colored pencils, write the name of each color on the picture.* If needed, model by drawing a picture on the board. When most students have finished, write *Longest wavelength* and *Shortest wavelength* on the board. Tell students to label their pictures with information about the longest wavelength and the shortest wavelength.

## REACHING ALL STUDENTS: Visual and Kinesthetic Learners

Have students close their eyes and picture a rainbow in their minds. *What is the weather like? Where do you see the rainbow? Why does a rainbow appear?* Ask students to visualize the array of colors. Call out the colors from top to bottom. (red, orange, yellow, green, blue, indigo, violet) Then have students draw rainbows and share them in pairs.

**Organize Information** Have students do a sequence diagram of light refracting in an aquarium using the information on page 222. Then have them draw an aquarium picture in their notebooks under their sequence. The sequence diagram might look like this:

### Refraction

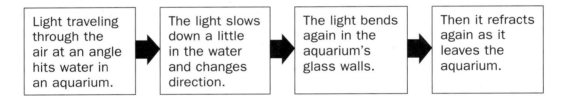

| Light traveling through the air at an angle hits water in an aquarium. | The light slows down a little in the water and changes direction. | The light bends again in the aquarium's glass walls. | Then it refracts again as it leaves the aquarium. |

---

### HISTORY CONNECTION: Telescopes and Galileo

Ask students to use the title and the illustration to predict what the text might be about. Read the text aloud, or call on a student to read it. Help students pronounce the dates. (sixteen oh nine, sixteen ten) Help students understand new words. Ask comprehension questions.

---

### Leaders in Science: Thomas Edison

Read the headings. Then point to the pictures and ask students, *Who is this man? What is he touching? What is he holding?* Read the text and the captions aloud, or call on individual students to read them. Help students with new words. Have students read the selection again to themselves or aloud in pairs or small groups. Ask comprehension questions. Discuss what modern tools and appliances we couldn't use without electricity.

### Before You Go On

Have pairs of students answer the first two questions. Have them write the questions and answers in their notebooks. Check answers before going on. Answer the third question together as a class.

**Answers**

1. Light refracts when it goes from one type of matter into another at an angle.
2. A prism refracts each wavelength of light at a different angle, from the longest wavelength to the shortest.
3. The rainbow is a refraction of light waves. The longest-length waves are at the top of the arc of the rainbow. The shortest-length waves are at the bottom.

For more information, go to www.longmanusa.com/science for links to interesting websites about sound and light.

## Review and Practice, pages 224–225

### Vocabulary

If students need help reviewing the vocabulary, see the Optional Vocabulary Activities (pages vii–viii). Have students complete the exercise individually. Check answers as a class.

**Answers**

| | | |
|---|---|---|
| 1. refraction | 3. transparent | 5. opaque |
| 2. reflection | 4. translucent | 6. electromagnetic wave |

### Check Your Understanding

Have students answer the questions individually, in pairs, or in small groups. If students need extra support, tell them to look at the information in their notebooks or allow students to look back at the text. Then have students share their answers with the class. Write the answers on the board.

**Answers**

1. The only electromagnetic wave we can see is visible light.
2. You can't see yourself in an uneven surface because the light waves bounce off at different angles.
3. The color of light depends on wavelength and frequency.
4. A white shirt reflects all the different wavelengths. It reflects red, orange, yellow, green, blue, and violet.

### Apply Science Skills

**Science Reading Strategy: Draw a Picture** Read the instructions aloud, or call on a student to read them. Have students reread the last paragraph on page 219, and then look at the photo of the flashlight and the beaker of milky water on page 212.

Have students complete their drawings individually or in pairs. Circulate to help and encourage students. Have them show and explain their drawings in small groups.

**Using Visuals: Wave Diagrams** Read the instructions aloud, or call on individual students to read them. Have students reread silently, if helpful. Ask comprehension questions to review concepts. Have students study the diagrams for a few minutes. Encourage them to reread the second paragraph on page 218, if helpful. Then have pairs ask and answer the questions. Have them write their answers in their notebooks. Then elicit the information and write it on the board.

> **Answers**
> 1. You can see a reflection of yourself in a smooth surface.
> 2. When light waves hit an uneven surface, they bounce off in different directions.
> 3. Possible answers: Smooth surfaces: glass, clear water, veneered wood, metal, and very hard plastic. Uneven surfaces: clothing, unfinished wood, and cloth.

## Discuss

Read the discussion questions aloud. Have students discuss the questions in small groups. Circulate to help and comment on student responses. Allow time for students to share their answers with the class. Do a class survey on which rainbow color is the class favorite.

 Workbook pages 107–108 may now be assigned.

## Evaluation

### Self-Assessment Questions

Write the following questions on the board. Have students respond in their notebooks. Encourage students to share their responses in small groups or as a class.
1. How can drawing a picture help me in reading?
2. How can wave diagrams help me understand information?
3. What was difficult for me in this lesson?
4. What was easy for me in this lesson?
5. What was most enjoyable in this lesson?

# Unit Review, pages 226–227

## Warm Up

Have pairs of students list the main ideas in Unit 6. Ask students to use the reading selection headings to group the main ideas. Alternatively, students may organize the main ideas in an idea map.

Ask pairs to exchange their completed list or word web. Each pair should review their newly acquired list to see if any important information is missing. If information is missing, the pair should add it.

## Vocabulary

Have students answer questions individually, with a partner, or in small groups, depending on how much support they need. Check answers as a class as you write the correct answers on the board.

> **Answers**
> 1. Vibrations make sound waves.
> 2. Vibrations travel through the air as sound waves.
> 3. Sound waves bouncing off a hard surface make echoes.
> 4. Light bouncing off a surface is called reflection.
> 5. The bending of light is called refraction.
> 6. Light waves have electrical and magnetic energy.
> 7. The loudness or softness of sound is called volume.
> 8. How high or low something sounds is its pitch.
> 9. Pitch is caused by the frequency of the sound waves.
> 10. Light can go all the way through transparent material.
> 11. Opaque matter absorbs some light and reflects the rest.
> 12. Frosted glass is translucent material.

## Check Your Understanding

Have students work individually, with a partner, or in small groups, depending on how much support they need. Check answers as a class as you write the correct answers on the board.

> **Answers**
> 1. False. Sound travels fastest through solids.
> 2. True
> 3. True
> 4. False. You can see yourself in a mirror because the light is reflected.
> 5. True

## Extension Project

For this project you'll need a flashlight and a prism. Read the instructions aloud, or call on a student to read them. Have students gather around the prism. Darken the room and have a student shine the flashlight through the prism. Ask, *What colors can you see? Why can you see these colors?* (The prism refracts, or bends, each wavelength at a different angle.) *What color has the longest wavelength?* (red) *Which color has the shortest wavelength?* (violet) Have students use crayons or colored pencils to draw their pictures.

## Apply Science Skills

**Using Visuals: Wave Diagrams** Read the instructions aloud, or call on a student to read them. Give students a few moments to study the diagram. Then, individually or in pairs, have students copy the diagram and complete the exercise. Remind students that they need to label the diagram as well as answer the questions. Check answers as a class as you write the correct answers on the board.

> **Answers**
> Diagram labels: (1) Radio waves (2) Infrared rays (3) Visible light
> (4) Ultraviolet rays (5) X rays (6) Gamma rays
> **1.** A toaster uses infrared rays.
> **2.** A doctor uses X rays.
> **3.** We can see only visible light waves.

## Read More About It

Bring at least one of the suggested books to class. Show the cover and some of the inside pages to students as a preview. Ask students to predict what the book is about. Read an excerpt aloud to the class. Then ask several comprehension questions. Read the excerpt again before calling on students to answer the questions. Encourage students to find this book or another suggested book in their school library or local bookstore.

Workbook pages 109–110 may now be assigned.

## Unit Experiment, pages 228–229
### How Does Light Reflect and Refract?

## Preview

Call on a student to read the experiment question aloud. Have students predict what they might be doing. Read aloud the introduction, purpose, and materials, or have individual students read them. Help students with new words. Make sure that students understand the experiment.

## Do the Experiment

For this experiment, you'll need to bring to class the items pictured. Ideally, students perform this exercise in medium-sized groups. If you have limited resources, you could do each experiment as a class.

Ask, *How does light reflect and refract? By doing these experiments, we can see for ourselves. It will help us understand.* Read each of the What to Do instructions aloud, or have a student read them. Ask comprehension questions so that you know students understand what to do. Be sure to ask if they have any questions. Have students perform each step of the experiment and record their observations in the data table on Workbook page 111.

Workbook page 111 may now be assigned.

The completed data table might look like this:

| Data Table | |
|---|---|
| **Step** | **Observation** |
| 1 | The light waves bounce back at the exact opposite angle they came from. |
| 2 | The pencil looks as if it is bending. |
| 3 | The objects change shape, especially near the sides of the glass. |
| 4 | The CD has rainbow colors on it. |

Have students answer the questions in Draw Conclusions by writing them on the Workbook page. Elicit conclusions from the class and write them on the board.

**Answers**
1. The light waves bounced back at the opposite angle. When light waves hit a smooth surface, they bounce back at the same angle but in the opposite direction.
2. An object in the water prevented the light waves from going straight through. They hit the water and were refracted.
3. The light moving through the water refracted and distorted the image of what we saw.
4. When the light hit the CD, it separated into different wavelengths.

 Workbook page 112 may now be assigned.

# Workbook Answer Key

## GETTING STARTED: INTRODUCTION
(pages 1–16)

### What Is Science?
(page 1)

**A.**

1. c    3. b    5. a
2. d    4. e

**B.**

1. The world      4. Nonliving things
2. Scientists     5. Living things
3. Science

**C.**

*left:* living thing
*middle:* nonliving thing
*right:* living thing

### The Sciences
(page 2)

**A.**

1. f    3. b    5. c
2. e    4. a

**B.**

Sentences will vary.

**C.**

1. plants     4. planets
2. rocks      5. rocks
3. animals    6. electricity

### The Sciences
(pages 3–4)

**A.**

**Top row:** life science, earth science, life science

**Bottom row:** life science, earth science, physical science

**B.**

**The Sciences**

life science ←→ Possible example: studying frogs

earth science ←→ Possible example: studying the environment

physical science ←→ Possible example: studying electricity

**C.**

1. c    3. b    5. b
2. b    4. a

### The Scientific Method
(pages 5–6)

**A.**

Step 1 ←→ Ask questions.
Step 2 ←→ Make a hypothesis.
Step 3 ←→ Test the hypothesis.
Step 4 ←→ Observe.
Step 5 ←→ Draw conclusions.

**B.**

1. d    3. e    5. c
2. a    4. b

**C.**

Sentences will vary.

**D.**

1. F    3. T    5. F
2. T    4. F

### Safety
(pages 7–8)

**A.**

**Top row:** d, b, e
**Middle row:** c, a, g
**Bottom row:** h, f

**B.**

1. d    3. a    5. b
2. e    4. c

**C.**

1. T    3. F    5. F
2. F    4. T

**D.**

1. understand    4. clean
2. hot           5. teacher
3. electricity

### Practicing the Scientific Method (pages 9–10)

**Experiment Log: How Does Water Move Inside a Flower?**

Completed logs will vary. Possible completed log:

**Step 1: Ask questions.**
How does water get to the petals of a flower?

**Step 2: Make a hypothesis.**
I think water moves up the stem. (Drawings will vary.)

**Step 3: Test your hypothesis.**
I will do the experiment on page 17.

**Step 4: Observe.**
The petals have lines of color in them. (Drawings will vary but should show lines of color in the flowers' petals.)

**Step 5: Draw conclusions.**
Water moves inside flowers through their stems.

### Science Tools
(pages 11–12)

**A.**

1. microscope     4. balance
2. stopwatch      5. camera
3. thermometer    6. hand lens

**B.**

1. e    4. f    7. d
2. a    5. h    8. b
3. g    6. c

**C.**

Sentences will vary.

**D.**

1. ruler          4. telescope
2. hand lens      5. microscope
3. thermometer

### Visuals
(pages 13–14)

1. diagram
2. micrograph
3. illustration
4. sectional diagram
5. photograph
6. chart
7. pie chart
8. cycle diagram

### More Review and Practice
(pages 15–16)

**Vocabulary**

**A.**

1. energy            7. world
2. stopwatch         8. life science
3. science           9. environment
4. microscope        10. matter
5. nonliving things  11. hypothesis
6. balance

| | | |
|---|---|---|
| 1. T | 5. T | 9. T |
| 2. F | 6. F | 10. F |
| 3. F | 7. F | |
| 4. T | 8. T | |

## Apply Science Skills
### Science Reading Strategy: Preview and Predict

1. Answers will vary. Possible answer: The pictures show different things that scientists study.
2. The picture of the koala in the tree shows living things.
3. The picture of the ice cube shows a nonliving thing.
4. Answers will vary. Possible answer: I will learn about living and nonliving things.

# UNIT 1: LESSON 1
(pages 17–22)

## Before You Read
(pages 17–20)

### Vocabulary (page 17)

**A.**

1. petals ←→ protect the inner parts of a flower
2. roots ←→ take in water for the plant
3. seeds ←→ can grow into new plants
4. stem ←→ holds the plant up
5. soil ←→ holds water and nutrients

**B.**
Sentences will vary.

**C.**

| | |
|---|---|
| 1. soil | 4. petals |
| 2. Seeds | 5. Roots |
| 3. leaves | |

**D.**

| | | |
|---|---|---|
| 1. T | 3. T | 5. F |
| 2. F | 4. F | |

## Science Skills
(pages 18–20)

### Science Reading Strategy: Main Idea and Details (page 18)

**Main Idea:** Insects and other animals are very important to plants.
**Detail:** Plants produce flowers that attract insects.

**Detail:** Insects pollinate the plants.
**Detail:** Animals eat the fruit.
**Detail:** Animals drop the seeds in the soil.

### Using Visuals: Diagrams (pages 19–20)

**A.**

1. A diagram is a drawing with labels.
2. This diagram shows the parts of a flower.
3. I see three labeled parts: male parts, female part, and petal.
4. Answers will vary. Possible answer: The diagram shows what the parts of a flower look like.
5. Answers will vary. Possible answer: I can give this diagram the title "Parts of a Flower."

**B.**

| | | |
|---|---|---|
| 1. c | 3. b | 5. a |
| 2. a | 4. c | |

## Lesson 1: More Review and Practice
(pages 21–22)

### Vocabulary

| | |
|---|---|
| 1. petals | 4. stem |
| 2. soil | 5. Roots |
| 3. Leaves | |

### Vocabulary in Context

| | |
|---|---|
| 1. soil | 4. stems |
| 2. seeds | 5. leaves |
| 3. roots | |

### Check Your Understanding

| | | |
|---|---|---|
| 1. b | 3. c | 5. c |
| 2. b | 4. a | |

## Apply Science Skills
### Science Reading Strategy: Main Idea and Details

**Main Idea:** The stem does many things for a plant.
**Details:** It holds the plant up. It also holds up the plant's leaves.
It carries water and food from place to place inside the plant.

### Using Visuals: Diagrams

| | |
|---|---|
| 1. Flower | 3. Leaf |
| 2. Stem | 4. Roots |

# UNIT 1: LESSON 2
(pages 23–28)

## Before You Read
(pages 23–26)

### Vocabulary (page 23)

**A.**

1. pollination ←→ passing pollen from flower to flower
2. germination ←→ a new plant beginning to grow from a seed
3. photosynthesis ←→ how a plant makes food
4. pollen ←→ yellow powder on a male flower part
5. energy ←→ heat and light
6. insects ←→ small animals such as bees and butterflies

**B.**
Sentences will vary.

**C.**

| | | |
|---|---|---|
| 1. T | 3. F | 5. F |
| 2. F | 4. T | |

**D.**

| | | |
|---|---|---|
| 1. e | 3. a | 5. c |
| 2. d | 4. b | |

## Science Skills
(pages 24–26)

### Science Reading Strategy: Compare and Contrast (page 24)

**B.**

**Water Lily**
grows in fresh water
has broad, flat leaves
has stems underwater

**Both**
belong to the plant kingdom
have roots
use photosynthesis to make food
have flowers

**Cactus**
grows in the desert
has long, thin leaves called spines
has stems above the ground

### Science Reading Strategy: Compare and Contrast (page 25)

**Apple**
is mostly round
has hard flesh
grows in cool climates

**Both**
are fruits
are sweet and juicy
are good to eat
contain seeds

**Papaya**
is shaped like a pear
has soft flesh
grows in warm climates

## Using Visuals: Cycle Diagrams (page 26)

1. The seeds come from inside the fruit.
2. They land on the ground. Some start to grow.
3. After the tree grows, the flowers bloom.
4. Flowers bloom before the fruit forms.
5. The fruit falls off the tree.

## Lesson 2:
## More Review and Practice
**(pages 27–28)**

### Vocabulary

1. photosynthesis
2. energy
3. pollen
4. germination
5. pollination

### Vocabulary in Context

1. Photosynthesis is the process plants use to make food.
2. T
3. T
4. The process of new plants growing from seeds is called germination.
5. Pollination is when insects pass pollen from flower to flower.

### Check Your Understanding

1. c     3. a     5. c
2. b     4. b

## Apply Science Skills
**Science Reading Strategy:**
**Compare and Contrast**
**Lemon**
has many small seeds
tastes sour

**Both**
are fruits
produce flowers
begin life as seeds

**Peach**
has one big seed
tastes sweet

## Unit 1: Unit Review
**(pages 29–30)**

### Vocabulary

**A.**

1. a     5. g     9. e
2. d     6. k     10. i
3. f     7. j
4. b     8. c

**B.**
Sentences will vary.

### Vocabulary in Context

1. insects
2. pollen
3. energy
4. photosynthesis
5. germination

## Apply Science Skills
**Using Visuals: Diagrams**

1. Flower        5. Female part
2. Stem          6. Petal
3. Leaf          7. Male parts
4. Roots

## UNIT 2: LESSON 1
**(pages 33–38)**

## Before You Read
**(pages 33–36)**

### Vocabulary (page 33)

**A.**

1. survive ⟷ means to stay alive
2. traits ⟷ facts about an animal
3. carnivore ⟷ eats only other animals
4. herbivore ⟷ eats only plants
5. omnivore ⟷ eats both plants and animals

**B.**
Sentences will vary.

**C.**

1. species        4. trait
2. herbivore      5. omnivore
3. carnivore      6. survive

**D.**

1. lion           3. survive
2. species        4. horse

## Science Skills
**(pages 34–36)**

**Science Reading Strategy:**
**Use What You Know (page 34)**

**A.**
Word webs will vary. Possible answers:

**Cats**

| kinds | bodies |
| --- | --- |
| cheetahs | furry |
| lions | four legs |
| house cats | tail |

| food | homes |
| --- | --- |
| cat food | forests |
| meat | grasslands |
| milk | people's homes |

## Using Visuals: Photographs (page 35)

1. The orangutan is an herbivore. The orangutan is eating bananas.
2. The lioness is a carnivore. She is running.
3. They both have fur, or hair.
4. The lioness needs to move faster because she hunts for food. She eats other animals.

## Using Visuals: Photographs (page 36)

1. c     3. b     5. c
2. b     4. a

## Lesson 1:
## More Review and Practice
**(pages 37–38)**

### Vocabulary

1. herbivore
2. survive
3. omnivore
4. traits
5. carnivore
**Secret word:** human

### Vocabulary in Context

1. species        4. herbivores
2. trait          5. survive
3. carnivores

### Check Your Understanding

1. b     3. b
2. c     4. a

## Apply Science Skills
### Science Reading Strategy:
### Use What You Know

Word webs will vary. Possible answers:

**Birds**

| kinds | food |
|-------|------|
| pelicans | seeds |
| cardinals | insects |
| hawks | fish |

### Using Visuals: Photographs

Answers will vary. Possible answers:

1. I think this bird lives near water because there is water in the picture.
2. This bird's beak is large and curved.
3. I think this bird uses its long neck to get food in the water.
4. This flamingo has pink feathers, wings, long legs, and a long neck.
5. I think the flamingo walks and flies.

## UNIT 2: LESSON 2
### (pages 39–44)

## Before You Read
### (pages 39–42)

**Vocabulary (page 39)**

**A.**

1. communicate ←→ use bodies and sounds
2. amphibians ←→ animals such as frogs
3. reptiles ←→ animals such as snakes and lizards
4. invertebrates ←→ animals without backbones
5. mammals ←→ animals such as dogs and humans

**B.**

Sentences will vary.

**C.**

| 1. F | 3. T | 5. F |
|------|------|------|
| 2. T | 4. F | |

**D.**

| 1. c | 3. e | 5. b |
|------|------|------|
| 2. d | 4. a | |

## Science Skills
### (pages 40–42)

**Science Reading Strategy:**
**Key Sentences (page 40)**

**A.**

Key sentences:

All zebras are mammals.
There are three species.
All zebra species have stripes.
Zebras are herbivores.

**B.**

**Zebras**

All zebras are mammals.
There are three species.
All zebra species have stripes.
Zebras are herbivores.

### Using Visuals: Pie Charts (page 41)

1. This pie chart shows three species of zebras.
2. The plains zebra is the species with the largest number of zebras.
3. The Grevy's zebra is the species with the smallest number of zebras.
4. The pie chart shows 100 percent of the zebras in Africa.
5. I think the Grevy's zebra is endangered. There are fewer of them.

### Using Visuals: Pie Charts (page 42)

1. 15 percent of reef fish are omnivores.
2. 74 percent of reef fish are carnivores.
3. 11 percent of reef fish are herbivores.
4. The omnivores and herbivores together make up 26 percent.
5. The carnivore group is the largest.

## Lesson 2:
## More Review and Practice
### (pages 43–44)

**Vocabulary**

| 1. reptiles | 4. amphibians |
|-------------|---------------|
| 2. mammals | 5. vertebrates |
| 3. invertebrates | |

**Vocabulary in Context**

| 1. T | 3. F | 5. T |
|------|------|------|
| 2. F | 4. F | |

**Check Your Understanding**

| 1. c | 3. b | 5. b |
|------|------|------|
| 2. a | 4. c | |

## Apply Science Skills
### Science Reading Strategy:
### Key Sentences

**Birds**

Birds live on land.
All birds hatch from eggs.
All birds care for their young.
All birds have wings.
All birds have feathers.

### Using Visuals: Pie Charts

1. 20%
2. 80%
3. a. yes
   b. no
   c. no

## Unit 2: Unit Review
### (pages 45–46)

**Vocabulary**

1. all species ←→ communicate
2. carnivores ←→ meat eaters
3. reptiles ←→ scales or plates and lungs
4. invertebrates ←→ have no backbones
5. amphibians ←→ gills and fins at birth
6. mammals ←→ birth live young
7. to survive → animals need water
8. omnivores ←→ meat and plant eaters

Sentences will vary.

**Vocabulary in Context**

1. omnivores
2. Carnivores
3. Invertebrates
4. vertebrates
5. survive

## Apply Science Skills
### Science Reading Strategy:
### Key Sentences

**Fish**

Fish are the biggest group of vertebrates.
All fish live in salt water or fresh water.
Many fish are endangered.
All fish need clean water, shelter, and food to survive.

# UNIT 3: LESSON 1
(pages 49–54)

## Before You Read
(pages 49–52)

### Vocabulary (page 49)

**A.**

1. c    3. d    5. b
2. a    4. e

**B.**

Sentences will vary.

**C.**

1. metamorphic    4. mineral
2. volcano    5. igneous
3. Sedimentary

**D.**

1. F. A diamond is clear and hard.
2. T
3. F. Igneous rock is made from hot liquid rock.
4. T
5. F. Hot liquid rock erupts out of a volcano.

## Science Skills
(pages 50–52)

### Science Reading Strategy: Ask Questions (page 50)

**A.**

Questions and answers will vary. Possible questions and answers:

**What:**

Q: What is the outermost layer of the earth called?

A: The outermost layer of the earth is called the crust.

Q: What is the crust like?

A: The crust is like the shell of an egg.

**Where:**

Q: Where on earth do we live?

A: We live on the crust.

Q: Where do the heavier materials end up?

A: The heavier materials end up deep inside the earth.

**Why:**

Q: Why is the crust like the shell of an egg?

A: The crust is like the shell of an egg because it is thin compared to the other layers.

Q: Why do the heavier materials end up deep inside the earth?

A: The heavier materials end up deep inside the earth because they sink down.

**How:**

Q: How many layers does the earth have?

A: The earth has four layers.

Q: How thick is the crust?

A: The crust is 3–25 miles thick.

### Science Reading Strategy: Ask Questions (page 51)

**A.**

Questions and answers will vary. Possible questions and answers:

**What:**

Q: What are several common properties of minerals?

A: Minerals are found in the earth, they are nonliving, they are made up of specific groups of atoms, they are solid, and they have crystals.

Q: What are minerals made up of?

A: Minerals are made up of specific groups of atoms.

**When:**

Q: When did humans discover some of these minerals?

A: Humans discovered some of these minerals a very long time ago.

**Where:**

Q: Where are minerals found?

A: Minerals are found in the earth.

Q: Where do minerals such as gold, silver, copper, and iron lie?

A: Minerals such as gold, silver, copper, and iron lie in the openings of ancient volcanoes.

**How:**

Q: How did humans use these minerals?

A: Humans used these minerals to make tools.

Q: How many common properties do minerals have?

A: Minerals have several common properties.

### Using Visuals: Sectional Diagrams (page 52)

1. I see four layers in this sectional diagram.
2. The two inner layers are made of metal.
3. The two outer layers are made of rock.
4. The second layer is made of soft rock.
5. The layer of solid metal is at the center of the earth.

## Lesson 1: More Review and Practice
(pages 53–54)

### Vocabulary

1. **p**roperties
2. igne**o**us
3. meta**m**orphic
4. se**d**imentary
5. vol**c**ano
6. mi**n**eral

**Secret word:** pumice

### Vocabulary in Context

1. volcano
2. igneous
3. metamorphic

### Check Your Understanding

1. a    3. c
2. b    4. c

## Apply Science Skills
### Science Reading Strategy: Ask Questions

Questions and answers will vary. Possible questions and answers:

**What:**

Q: What is the first layer of earth?

A: The first layer of earth is the crust.

Q: What is the mantle made of?

A: The mantle is made of hot, soft rock.

**Why:**

Q: Why can't scientists go inside the last three layers to study them?

A: The last three layers are too deep and too hot.

**Where:**

Q: Where is liquid metal found?

A: Liquid metal is found in the outer core.

Q: Where is solid metal found?

A: Solid metal is found in the inner core.

**How:**

Q: How many layers does the earth have?

A: The earth has four layers.

## Using Visuals: Sectional Diagrams

1. The diagram shows a volcano erupting.
2. Hot liquid rock and smoke are coming out of the volcano.
3. Extrusive igneous rock and intrusive igneous rock are two types of igneous rock in the diagram.
4. No. Igneous rock cannot be made in any other way.
5. Yes, I think this volcano is active because there is smoke and hot liquid rock coming out of it.

## UNIT 3: LESSON 2
(pages 55–60)

## Before You Read
(pages 55–58)

### Vocabulary (page 55)

**A.**

1. weathering ←→ the breaking up of rock into pieces
2. geologist ←→ a person who studies rocks
3. erosion ←→ the movement of rocks and soil
4. earthquake ←→ a shaking of the ground
5. glacier ←→ a big sheet of ice

**B.**

Sentences will vary.

**C.**

1. T
2. F. Weathering is a process that causes rocks to break into pieces.
3. T
4. F. Wind, water, and glaciers can cause weathering/erosion.
5. F. A glacier is a big sheet of ice.

**D.**

1. earthquake
2. life science
3. sand
4. volcano
5. igneous

## Science Skills
(pages 56–58)

### Science Reading Strategy: Cause and Effect (page 56)

**A.**

1. Heavy rain or an earthquake can cause a mudslide.
2. Some effects of a mudslide are damage to cities, houses, trees, and roads. Sometimes people die.

**B.**

**Cause:** Mudslide

**Effects:** Damages cities
Destroys houses
Destroys trees
Damages roads
People die

### Science Reading Strategy: Cause and Effect (page 57)

**A.**

1. Deforestation is when people cut down a lot of trees.
2. Deforestation can cause soil erosion.

**B.**

**Cause:** Deforestation

**Effects:** Mudslides
Erosion of the soil
Animals go to other locations
Land is no longer useful

### Using Visuals: Photo Sequences (page 58)

**B.**

1. First the volcano erupts. (right photo)
2. Then the hot liquid rock cools and hardens, forming igneous rock. (left photo)
3. Over time, the igneous rock may form a large dome. (bottom photo)

## Lesson 2:
## More Review and Practice
(pages 59–60)

### Vocabulary

1. geologist
2. glacier
3. earthquake
4. weathering
5. erosion

### Vocabulary in Context

1. geologist
2. weathering
3. earthquakes

### Check Your Understanding

1. a       3. a
2. c       4. c

## Apply Science Skills
### Science Reading Strategy: Cause and Effect

**Cause:** Mountaintops are exposed to air, wind, and water.

**Effect:** Over time, these forces cause the rock surface to break up into pieces.

**Cause:** Many mountains are covered by lichens.

**Effect:** Lichens produce chemicals that cause rock to break apart.

### Using Visuals: Photo Sequences (page 60)

1. b., c., a.
2. This photo sequence shows the volcano Mount St. Helens before, during, and after an eruption.

## Unit 3: Unit Review
(pages 61–62)

### Vocabulary

1. weathering ←→ the breaking down of rock
2. igneous ←→ rock formed when volcanoes erupt
3. mineral ←→ solid substance that has crystals
4. erosion ←→ the moving of rocks and soil
5. sedimentary ←→ rock that can have fossils in it
6. metamorphic ←→ rock formed when rock changes
7. properties ←→ traits
8. glacier ←→ big sheet of ice

Sentences will vary.

### Vocabulary in Context

1. properties
2. glacier
3. weathering
4. volcano
5. Metamorphic

## Apply Science Skills
### Science Reading Strategy: Ask Questions

Questions and answers will vary. Possible questions and answers:

**What:**

Q: What are diamonds?
A: Diamonds are carbon deposits that are exposed to heat and pressure over a very long time.

Q: What are volcanic pipes?

A: Volcanic pipes are openings in old volcanoes.

**Where:**

Q: Where do diamonds come from?

A: Diamonds come from deep in the earth.

Q: Where does the hot liquid rock push the diamond crystals?

A: The hot liquid rock pushes the diamond crystals through the mantle toward the earth's crust.

**Why:**

Q: Why are diamond crystals so hard?

A: Diamond crystals are so hard because they are exposed to heat and pressure over a very long time.

**How:**

Q: How do diamond crystals come closer to the surface?

A: Diamond crystals come closer to the surface through volcanic pipes.

Q: How do diamond crystals get pushed through the mantle toward the earth's crust?

A: Diamond crystals get pushed through the mantle toward the earth's crust by the hot liquid rock.

# UNIT 4: LESSON 1
## (pages 65–70)

## Before You Read
### (pages 65–68)

### Vocabulary (page 65)

**A.**

1. solar system ←→ nine planets orbiting the sun
2. atmosphere ←→ made of gases
3. galaxy ←→ a group of stars, planets, gases, and dust
4. asteroids ←→ pieces of rock and metal
5. comet ←→ ball of ice and dust
6. orbit ←→ move around the sun

**B.**

Sentences will vary.

**C.**

1. orbits
2. stars
3. gases
4. ice
5. Asteroids

**D.**

1. F. Planets orbit the sun.
2. T
3. T

4. F. Galaxies are groups of stars and planets.
5. T

## Science Skills
### (pages 66–68)

### Science Reading Strategy: Reread (page 66)

**B.**

1. We live on the planet Earth.
2. Oxygen is an important gas that is part of Earth's atmosphere.
3. Earth is part of our solar system.
4. There are nine planets in our solar system.
5. Planets, asteroids, and comets orbit the sun.

**C.**

Sentences will vary.

### Using Visuals: Illustrations (page 67)

1. Scientists use big telescopes with a special camera.
2. Scientists can't include all nine planets in the same photo because the planets in our solar system are so far away from one another.
3. An artist can use photos as models.
4. I can see nine planets in this picture.
5. The planets, from left to right, are Mercury, Venus, Earth, Mars, Jupiter, Saturn, Uranus, Neptune, and Pluto.

### Using Visuals: Illustrations (page 68)

1. c   3. a   5. c
2. b   4. a

## Lesson 1:
## More Review and Practice
### (pages 69–70)

### Vocabulary

1. **g**alaxy
2. **a**steroids
3. atmo**s**phere
4. com**e**t
5. **s**olar system

**Secret word:** gases

### Vocabulary in Context

1. solar system
2. galaxy
3. Asteroids/Comets

4. comets/asteroids
5. atmosphere

### Check Your Understanding

1. We live in the Milky Way galaxy.
2. The path that each planet moves in is called an orbit.
3. The four planets closest to the sun are Mercury, Venus, Earth, and Mars.
4. The five planets farthest from the sun are Jupiter, Saturn, Uranus, Neptune, and Pluto.

## Apply Science Skills
### Science Reading Strategy: Reread

1. Asteroids are pieces of rock and metal.
2. Asteroids in our solar system orbit the sun between Mars and Jupiter.
3. Comets are made of ice, frozen gases, and dust.
4. When the sun heats up a comet, the ice turns into a cloud of gases with a long tail.
5. Comets reflect light from the sun.

### Using Visuals: Illustrations

1. This illustration shows the Milky Way galaxy and some of the planets in our solar system.
2. Answers will vary, but some students will recognize Earth, Mars, and Saturn.
3. These planets belong to our solar system.
4. This illustration is not realistic because we can see more planets than is normally possible. Also, the planets are enlarged.

# UNIT 4: LESSON 2
## (pages 71–76)

## Before You Read
### (pages 71–74)

### Vocabulary (page 71)

**A.**

1. constellation ←→ a star pattern
2. telescope ←→ a tool people use to see objects in space
3. astronomers ←→ scientists who study objects in space
4. universe ←→ everything in space
5. trillion ←→ a very large number

**B.**

Sentences will vary.

**C.**

1. F. Astronomers study objects in space.
2. T
3. T
4. F. A telescope is a tool used by astronomers.
5. F. A trillion is a very large number.

**D.**

1. c    3. b    5. a
2. d    4. e

## Science Skills
(pages 72–74)

### Using Visuals: Deep Space Photos
(page 74)

1. The photo shows thousands of stars in deep space.
2. The objects in the photo are so small because they are very far away.
3. The colors of the stars tell me how hot or cold they are.
4. My picture is an illustration.
5. This is a picture of part of the universe because it is impossible to take a picture of the whole universe.

## Lesson 2:
## More Review and Practice
(pages 75–76)

### Vocabulary

1. astronomer    4. trillion
2. universe    5. constellation
3. telescope

### Vocabulary in Context

1. F. An astronomer studies objects in space.
2. T
3. F. A constellation is a group of stars that makes a pattern.
4. T

### Check Your Understanding

1. b    3. c
2. b    4. a

## Apply Science Skills
### Using Visuals: Deep Space Photos

1. I see galaxies in the photo.
2. I see spiral and elliptical galaxies.

3. I see yellow, orange, blue, red, and white.
4. I can tell it is a deep space photo because I can see whole galaxies.

## Unit 4: Unit Review
(pages 77–78)

### Vocabulary

1. astronomer ←→ scientist who studies objects in space
2. universe ←→ everything in space
3. comet ←→ ball of ice and dust
4. orbit ←→ move around the sun
5. solar system ←→ planets orbiting a sun
6. atmosphere ←→ made up of gases
7. constellations ←→ patterns made by stars
8. asteroid ←→ piece of rock and metal

Sentences will vary.

### Vocabulary in Context

1. universe    4. solar system
2. astronomer    5. galaxy
3. telescope

## Apply Science Skills
### Science Reading Strategy: Reread

**A.**

1. The sun is at the center of our solar system.

**B.**

2. Every solar system has a star at its center.
3. Our solar system is part of the Milky Way galaxy.
4. There are millions of solar systems in our galaxy.
5. There are trillions of galaxies in the universe.

## UNIT 5: LESSON 1
(pages 81–86)

## Before You Read
(pages 81–84)

### Vocabulary (page 81)

**A.**

1. c    3. a    5. f
2. d    4. b    6. e

**B.**

Sentences will vary.

**C.**

1. matter    4. volume
2. atoms    5. Mass
3. measure

**D.**

1. F. Atoms are very small things that make up matter.
2. T
3. F. You can use a measuring cup to measure volume.
4. F. You can use a balance to measure mass.
5. T

## Science Skills
(pages 82–84)

### Science Reading Strategy: Facts and Examples (page 82)

**Fact:** Wood has low density.

**Example:** If you throw a piece of wood in the water, it will float.

**Fact:** Iron has high density.

**Example:** If you throw a piece of iron in the water, it will sink to the bottom.

### Science Reading Strategy: Facts and Examples (page 83)

**Fact:** Everything around you is matter.

**Example:** My desk, my classmates, and the air I breathe are all matter.

**Fact:** Atoms are very tiny.

**Example:** Millions of atoms could fit on a tiny dot.

**Fact:** Each kind of matter has its own properties.

**Example:** Water is clear and has no color. It is a liquid. It freezes at 0° Celsius and boils at 100° Celsius.

### Using Visuals: Micrographs (page 84)

1. Sand is made of tiny rocks.
2. I can eat sugar and salt.
3. A snowflake is a crystal with six branches.
4. Answers will vary.
5. Answers will vary.

## Lesson 1:
## More Review and Practice
**(pages 85–86)**

### Vocabulary

1. ma**ss**
2. matt**er**
3. de**n**sity
4. atom**s**
5. volum**e**
6. mea**s**ure

**Secret word:** senses

### Vocabulary in Context

1. matter
2. atoms
3. measure
4. volume/density
5. density/volume

### Check Your Understanding

1. b    2. c    3. a    4. b

## Apply Science Skills
### Science Reading Strategy: Facts and Examples

**Fact:** Each type of matter has its own properties.

**Example:** Honey is sweet and it is a liquid.

**Fact:** Honey shares properties with other liquids.

**Example:** You can pour honey, and it takes the shape of its container.

### Using Visuals: Micrographs

1. Those atoms make sand.
2. Those atoms make the metal nickel.
3. Those atoms make graphite.
4. Drawings will vary.

## UNIT 5: LESSON 2
**(pages 87–92)**

## Before You Read
**(pages 87–90)**

### Vocabulary (page 87)

**A.**

1. c    3. e    5. b
2. d    4. a

**B.**

Sentences will vary.

**C.**

1. states        4. physical
2. melting       5. chemical
3. boiling

**D.**

1. F. There are three states of matter: solid, liquid, and gas.
2. T
3. F. The boiling point of water is 100° Celsius.
4. T
5. F. Water changing states is a physical change.

## Science Skills
**(pages 88–90)**

### Science Reading Strategy: Idea Maps (page 88)

**Measuring Matter**

**Mass** ⟷ Use a balance.

**Volume** ⟷ Use a container.

**Density** ⟷ Use a container and a balance.

### Science Reading Strategy: Idea Maps (page 89)

Answers will vary.

### Using Visuals: States of Matter Illustrations (page 90)

1. From left to right, the illustrations show a solid, a liquid, and a gas.
2. Each round shape represents an atom.
3. There is the most space between atoms in the gas state.
4. There is the least space between atoms in the solid state.
5. You would heat a liquid to change it into a gas.

## Lesson 2:
## More Review and Practice
**(pages 91–92)**

### Vocabulary

1. boiling point
2. chemical change
3. melting point
4. physical change
5. states

### Vocabulary in Context

1. states
2. melting point
3. boiling point
4. physical change
5. chemical change

### Check Your Understanding

1. b    2. a    3. c

## Apply Science Skills
### Science Reading Strategy: Idea Maps

**Properties of Matter**

**Solid:** Set shape, Set volume

**Liquid:** No set shape, Set volume

### Using Visuals: States of Matter Illustrations

1. Illustration a. is an example of a liquid.
2. Illustration b. is an example of a solid.
3. Illustration c. is an example of a gas.
4. The atoms move the fastest in the gas state.
5. The atoms move the slowest in the solid state.

## Unit 5: Unit Review
**(pages 93–94)**

### Vocabulary

1. chemical change ⟷ a different kind of matter is formed
2. physical change ⟷ matter changes shape or state
3. density ⟷ mass per unit of volume
4. melting point ⟷ temperature at which a solid melts
5. volume ⟷ the space matter takes up
6. atoms ⟷ very tiny things that make up matter
7. boiling point ⟷ temperature at which a liquid boils
8. mass ⟷ how much of something there is

Sentences will vary.

### Vocabulary in Context

1. Atoms        4. mass/volume
2. matter       5. volume/mass
3. measure

## Apply Science Skills
### Science Reading Strategy: Facts and Examples

**Fact:** Most things in nature are mixtures.

**Example:** Sand, ocean water, and soil are mixtures.

**Fact:** Anything you can combine is a mixture.

**Example:** Chocolate powder and milk form a mixture.

# UNIT 6: LESSON 1
(pages 97–102)

## Before You Read
(pages 97–100)

### Vocabulary (page 97)

**A.**

1. b    3. e    5. c
2. f    4. a    6. d

**B.**

Sentences will vary.

**C.**

1. sound waves    4. pitch
2. volume    5. frequency
3. echo

## Science Skills
(pages 98–100)

### Using Visuals: Charts (page 99)

1. A TV and a busy street have the same volume in decibels.
2. A shuttle taking off has the highest volume.
3. The sound of rain is louder than the sound of falling leaves.
4. A rock concert is 45 decibels louder than a TV.
5. I think high decibel levels are dangerous to my hearing, such as a rock concert or a plane taking off.

### Using Visuals: Charts (page 100)

1. A dog's range of hearing is closest to a human's.
2. Humans can hear sounds of the lowest frequency.
3. Dolphins have the widest range of hearing.
4. A beluga whale has a wider range of hearing than a bat.
5. The chicken's hearing range is the smallest.

# Lesson 1:
## More Review and Practice
(pages 101–102)

### Vocabulary

1. volume
2. frequency
3. sound waves
4. vibrations
5. echo

**Secret word:** music

### Vocabulary in Context

1. Pitch    3. vibrations
2. frequency    4. volume

### Check Your Understanding

1. a    3. c
2. c    4. b

## Apply Science Skills
### Science Reading Strategy: Act It Out

1. Yes, there is always an echo against any hard surface.
2. If the ball hit a pillow, there wouldn't be an echo. The sound would be absorbed.

### Using Visuals: Charts

1. Sound travels the fastest in steel.
2. Sound travels the slowest in dry, cold air.
3. Hard wood, glass, and steel are solids.
4. Sound travels faster in glass because sound travels more quickly through solids.
5. Sound travels faster in steel than in cold dry air because the atoms in steel are closer together and the vibrations can move more quickly.

# UNIT 6: LESSON 2
(pages 103–108)

## Before You Read
(pages 103–106)

### Vocabulary (page 103)

**A.**

1. b    3. d    5. f
2. a    4. e    6. c

**B.**

Sentences will vary.

**C.**

1. F. Opaque objects reflect light.
2. T
3. T
4. F. The moon is an opaque object.
5. F. When light waves bounce off a surface, we call it reflection.
6. T
7. T
8. F. Light is a type of electromagnetic wave.

## Science Skills
(pages 104–106)

### Using Visuals: Wave Diagrams (page 106)

1. The different types of waves on the diagram are radio waves, infrared rays, visible light, ultraviolet rays, X rays, and gamma rays.
2. Gamma rays have the highest frequency.
3. Radio waves have the longest wavelength.
4. Infrared rays have a long wavelength.
5. Yes, I do think that high-frequency waves can be harmful. Ultraviolet rays can burn your skin. X rays and gamma rays give off radiation.

# Lesson 2:
## More Review and Practice
(pages 107–108)

### Vocabulary

1. refraction
2. opaque
3. electromagnetic waves
4. transparent
5. reflection

### Vocabulary in Context

1. an electromagnetic
2. refracting
3. reflection
4. transparent
5. translucent

### Check Your Understanding

1. c    3. b
2. b    4. a

## Apply Science Skills
### Using Visuals: Wave Diagrams

1. When light waves hit a smooth surface, they bounce off in the opposite direction, creating a reflection.
2. The wave diagram of light hitting a smooth surface shows what happens when light waves hit a mirror's surface.
3. The wave diagram of light hitting an uneven surface shows what happens when light hits the surface of my clothing.

## Unit 6: Unit Review
### (pages 109–110)

### Vocabulary

1. electromagnetic waves ←——→ have their own energy
2. pitch ←——→ how low or high a sound is
3. frequency ←——→ how close together or far apart sound waves are
4. reflection ←——→ light waves bouncing off a surface
5. refraction ←——→ the bending of light
6. vibrations ←——→ movements up and down
7. volume ←——→ how soft or loud a sound is
8. opaque ←——→ light waves cannot travel through

Sentences will vary.

### Vocabulary in Context

1. pitch
2. volume
3. refraction
4. reflection
5. transparent

## Apply Science Skills
### Science Reading Strategies: Act It Out and Draw a Picture

Answers will vary. Possible answer: I see rainbow colors as the light of the flashlight shines on the water drops.

# Introduction to the Tests

Each unit has three tests: two Lesson Tests and an overall Unit Test. The tests cover key vocabulary, content, science skills, and include a writing section. The writing section should be scored holistically, using the four-point writing rubric below. Each response should receive a score from 0 to 4 points, with 4 points being the highest score. The Getting Started unit is an exception in that it has one test for the entire unit and no writing section. To calculate the scores, follow this procedure:

• The Lesson Tests have 11 items, each worth 1 point. The writing section is worth a maximum of 4 points. So the maximum score for a Lesson Test is 15 points.

• The Unit Tests have 21 items, each worth 1 point. The writing section is worth a maximum of 4 points. So the maximum score for a Unit Test is 25 points.

| Scoring the Writing Sections | |
|---|---|
| **Score** | **Description** |
| **4 points** | The paragraph is focused, well organized, and complete. There is a logical beginning, middle, and end. The paragraph begins with a main idea and gives details and/or examples that relate to the main idea. There is a demonstrated understanding of the content of the lesson or unit. There is a demonstrated command of spelling, capitalization, punctuation, grammar, usage, and sentence structure. The paragraph may contain some errors in writing conventions, but these errors do not detract from the overall fluency. |
| **3 points** | The paragraph as a whole is focused and mostly complete, but is not as well organized as a 4-point response. There is a main idea and some details and/or examples. There is an understanding of the content. There is a generally consistent command of spelling, capitalization, punctuation, grammar, usage, and sentence structure. Choice of words, phrases, and content vocabulary is appropriate. The paragraph may include minor errors in writing conventions, but these errors do not disrupt the fluency. |
| **2 points** | The paragraph shows some sense of focus in that it may have a main idea, but no details, or details, but no main idea. The student may shift from idea to idea without a logical transition. The paragraph may also include irrelevant information, repetition, and gaps in ideas, or simply list ideas with little development. There is only a vague understanding of the content. There is a limited command of writing conventions, and there are errors in spelling, capitalization, punctuation, grammar, usage, and sentence structure throughout the paragraph. These errors may weaken the overall fluency of the paragraph. |
| **1 point** | The paragraph as a whole is not focused and has little or no sense of completeness. There is no main idea and few details. The details that exist may be randomly presented or repeated. The paragraph may also include irrelevant ideas. There is little understanding of content or writing conventions. The errors that exist weaken the paragraph by causing an overall lack of fluency. |
| **0 points** | The paragraph is completely incorrect, irrelevant, or incoherent, or the student does not attempt to respond to the writing prompt at all. |

Copyright © 2006 Pearson Education, Inc. Duplication for classroom use is permitted.

# Getting Started: Introduction Test

## The Sciences

Choose the best answer. Circle the letter.

1. The study of plants and animals is _____.
   a. life science
   b. earth science
   c. computer science
   d. physical science

2. The study of the earth, the environment, and space is _____.
   a. computer science
   b. life science
   c. earth science
   d. physical science

3. The study of nonliving matter and energy is _____.
   a. earth science
   b. physical science
   c. computer science
   d. life science

## The Scientific Method

Choose the best answer. Circle the letter.

4. What is the first step in the scientific method?
   a. Drawing conclusions
   b. Testing a hypothesis
   c. Answering questions
   d. Asking questions

5. What is making a hypothesis?
   a. Drawing a conclusion
   b. Making a guess
   c. Asking a question
   d. Doing an experiment

Copyright © 2006 Pearson Education, Inc. Duplication for classroom use is permitted.

**6.** What is a good way to test a hypothesis?

    **a.** Do an experiment.

    **b.** Make a guess.

    **c.** Draw a conclusion.

    **d.** Ask a question.

**7.** Look at the picture. What is the scientist doing?

    **a.** Adding water

    **b.** Drawing conclusions

    **c.** Observing

    **d.** None of the above

**8.** What is drawing conclusions?

    **a.** Making a guess

    **b.** Doing an experiment

    **c.** Asking questions

    **d.** Deciding if the hypothesis is correct

## Safety

Choose the best answer. Circle the letter.

**9.** What do you need to be careful with?

    **a.** Scissors

    **b.** Electricity

    **c.** Hot things

    **d.** All of the above

**10.** Look at the picture. What do you need to do if glass breaks?

    **a.** Pick it up.

    **b.** Tell your teacher.

    **c.** Read the instructions carefully.

    **d.** All of the above.

Copyright © 2009 Pearson Education, Inc. Duplication for classroom use is permitted.

**11.** How do you carry scissors?

   **a.** Point them down.

   **b.** Point them up.

   **c.** Point them out.

   **d.** All of the above.

## Science Tools

Look at the picture next to each question. Choose the best answer. Circle the letter.

**12.** A _____ measures how heavy something is.

   **a.** ruler

   **b.** balance

   **c.** camera

   **d.** hand lens

**13.** A _____ measures how hot or cold something is.

   **a.** balance

   **b.** camera

   **c.** thermometer

   **d.** telescope

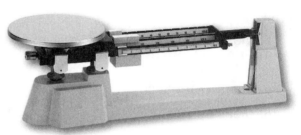

**14.** A _____ lets us see things far away in the sky.

   **a.** balance

   **b.** hand lens

   **c.** telescope

   **d.** stopwatch

**15.** A _____ lets us see very small things.

   **a.** ruler

   **b.** stopwatch

   **c.** thermometer

   **d.** microscope

Copyright © 2006 Pearson Education, Inc. Duplication for classroom use is permitted.

## Visuals

Look at the visual. Choose the best answer. Circle the letter.

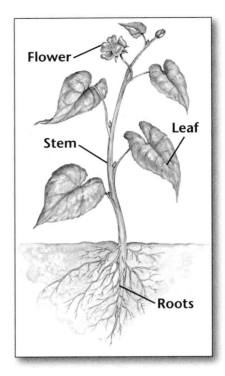

16. This is a _____ of a plant.

    **a.** diagram

    **b.** photograph

    **c.** micrograph

    **d.** chart

17. Scientists use visuals to _____.

    **a.** make guesses

    **b.** test a hypothesis

    **c.** share information

    **d.** measure time

## Science Reading Strategies

Choose the best answer. Circle the letter.

18. What do you look at when you **preview**?

    **a.** You look at the headings.

    **b.** You look at the pictures.

    **c.** You look at the words near the pictures.

    **d.** All of the above.

19. What do you do when you **predict**?

    **a.** You read the text carefully.

    **b.** You guess what you will learn about.

    **c.** You ask your teacher questions.

    **d.** You write in your notebook.

20. What can science reading strategies help you do?

    **a.** Understand and remember what you read

    **b.** Use the scientific method

    **c.** Keep your classmates and you safe

    **d.** Measure things

Copyright © 2006 Pearson Education, Inc. Duplication for classroom use is permitted

# Unit 1: Lesson 1 Test

## Key Words

Choose the best answer. Circle the letter.

**1.** Most plants have flowers, leaves, stems, and _____.

    **a.** soil

    **b.** roots

    **c.** spines

    **d.** lilies

**2.** A plant takes in water and nutrients from the _____.

    **a.** sun

    **b.** leaves

    **c.** petals

    **d.** soil

**3.** The plant makes food in the _____.

    **a.** roots

    **b.** petals

    **c.** leaves

    **d.** stems

**4.** The flower's main job is to make _____.

    **a.** seeds

    **b.** leaves

    **c.** stems

    **d.** roots

## Using Visuals

Look at the diagram. Choose the best answer. Circle the letter.

**5.** What protects the inside parts of the flower?

    **a.** The stem

    **b.** The petals

    **c.** The male parts

    **d.** The female part

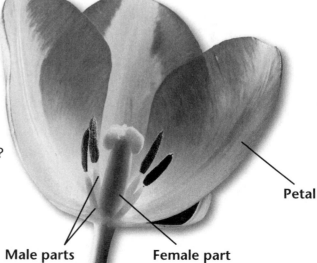

Petal

Male parts

Female part

Copyright © 2006 Pearson Education, Inc. Duplication for classroom use is permitted.

Name _____ Date _____

## Content

Choose the best answer. Circle the letter.

6. How are plants different from animals?

   a. Plants need food and water.

   b. Plants eat animals or other plants.

   c. Plants make their own food.

   d. All of the above.

7. What do roots do?

   a. They take in water from the soil.

   b. They take in nutrients from the soil.

   c. They keep the plant in the ground.

   d. All of the above.

8. What is **not** true about the stem?

   a. It holds the leaves up.

   b. It has seeds inside.

   c. It carries water to the leaves.

   d. It carries food from the leaves to other parts of the plant.

9. Where does a plant take in and give off gases?

   a. From the stem

   b. From the flower

   c. From the leaves

   d. From the roots

10. Look at the picture. What are these?

    a. Needles

    b. Petals

    c. Trunks

    d. Broad leaves

11. Which part of a flower becomes the fruit?

    a. The stem

    b. The petals

    c. The male parts

    d. The female part

## Writing

Write a paragraph about the parts of a plant. Include what each part does. Make sure your paragraph has a beginning, a middle, and an end.

Copyright © 2006 Pearson Education, Inc. Duplication for classroom use is permitted.

Copyright © 2006 Pearson Education, Inc. Duplication for classroom use is permitted.

Name _____ Date _____

# Unit 1: Lesson 2 Test

## Key Words

Choose the best answer. Circle the letter.

1. A plant makes food in a process called _____.

   **a.** germination

   **b.** pollination

   **c.** photosynthesis

   **d.** ecotourism

2. The yellow powder on the male part of a plant is _____.

   **a.** pollen

   **b.** energy

   **c.** fruit

   **d.** food

3. Insects move pollen in a process called _____.

   **a.** photosynthesis

   **b.** ecotourism

   **c.** germination

   **d.** pollination

4. The roots grow first in a process called _____.

   **a.** germination

   **b.** pollination

   **c.** photosynthesis

   **d.** ecotourism

## Using Visuals

Look at the diagram. Choose the **true** sentence. Circle the letter.

5. **a.** This diagram shows photosynthesis.

   **b.** This diagram shows the plant life cycle.

   **c.** This diagram shows carbon dioxide.

   **d.** This diagram shows fruit growing.

Name _____  Date _____

## Content

Choose the best answer. Circle the letter.

6. What is **not** true about photosynthesis?

   **a.** Plants use energy from the sun to make food.

   **b.** Plants change water and carbon dioxide into sugar and oxygen.

   **c.** Plants take in oxygen.

   **d.** The sugar is the plant's food.

7. When can the female part of a flower grow into a fruit?

   **a.** After pollination

   **b.** After germination

   **c.** After the plant breaks out of the hard shell

   **d.** None of the above

8. What is an example of a fruit?

   **a.** A banana

   **b.** A tomato

   **c.** Grains such as wheat and oats

   **d.** All of the above

9. How do seeds move?

   **a.** Some pollen gets on an insect's body.

   **b.** Wind, water, and animals carry them.

   **c.** The seeds give off gases.

   **d.** None of the above.

10. Look at the picture. What's inside a seed?

    **a.** Pollen

    **b.** Pinecones

    **c.** Carbon dioxide

    **d.** A new plant and stored food

11. What happens when a seed doesn't get water, heat, and light?

    **a.** A fruit begins to grow.

    **b.** A flower begins to grow.

    **c.** It dies.

    **d.** A new plant begins to grow.

## Writing

Write a paragraph about the life of a plant. Include key facts about pollination and germination. Make sure your paragraph has a beginning, a middle, and an end.

Copyright © 2006 Pearson Education, Inc. Duplication for classroom use is permitted

# Unit 1: Unit Test

## Key Words

Choose the best answer. Circle the letter.

1. Most seeds need water, heat, and nutrients to begin _____.
   a. germination
   b. making fruit
   c. pollination
   d. making flowers

2. A plant takes in water and nutrients with its _____.
   a. petals
   b. pollen
   c. roots
   d. male parts

3. The stem carries water to the _____.
   a. seeds
   b. leaves
   c. roots
   d. soil

4. A plant makes food in its leaves by _____.
   a. making fruit
   b. photosynthesis
   c. pollination
   d. germination

5. A fruit can grow after _____.
   a. letting out water vapor
   b. germination
   c. photosynthesis
   d. pollination

6. Look at the picture. The fruit protects the _____.
   a. seeds
   b. roots
   c. leaves
   d. petals

Copyright © 2006 Pearson Education, Inc. Duplication for classroom use is permitted.

Name _____ Date _____

## Content

Choose the best answer. Circle the letter.

**7.** What moves seeds to new places?

    **a.** Wind

    **b.** Water

    **c.** Animals

    **d.** All of the above

**8.** What grows first when a seed germinates?

    **a.** The root

    **b.** The flower

    **c.** The fruit

    **d.** The leaves

**9.** Look at the picture. What kind of leaves does this plant have?

    **a.** Spines

    **b.** Broad

    **c.** Petals

    **d.** Needles

**10.** What does a plant change water and carbon dioxide into?

    **a.** Soil

    **b.** Pollen

    **c.** Pinecones

    **d.** Sugar and oxygen

**11.** How are plants and animals different?

    **a.** Plants make their own food.

    **b.** Plants have roots to stay in one place.

    **c.** Plants take in carbon dioxide.

    **d.** All of the above.

**12.** What protects the male and female parts of a flower?

    **a.** The leaves

    **b.** The roots

    **c.** The petals

    **d.** The seed

Copyright © 2006 Pearson Education, Inc. Duplication for classroom use is permitted.

**13.** What is pollination?

    **a.** Pollen lands on the female part of a flower.

    **b.** Pollen lands on the petals.

    **c.** Pollen forms inside a fruit.

    **d.** Pollen falls to the ground.

**14.** Look at the picture. What usually carries pollen from flower to flower?

    **a.** Fruit

    **b.** Insects

    **c.** Seeds

    **d.** All of the above

**15.** What does the female part of a plant grow into?

    **a.** Fruit

    **b.** A flower

    **c.** Leaves

    **d.** The stem

**16.** What are tomatoes, wheat, and bananas?

    **a.** Vegetables

    **b.** Grain

    **c.** Fruit

    **d.** None of the above

## Reading Strategies

Choose the best answer. Circle the letter.

**17.** How do you find the **main idea and details**?

    **a.** Guess what you will learn about.

    **b.** Draw a picture and label the parts.

    **c.** Look for the most important idea and facts that support it.

    **d.** All of the above.

**18.** How can you **compare and contrast**?

    **a.** Think about how two things are the same.

    **b.** Think about how two things are different.

    **c.** Draw a Venn diagram.

    **d.** All of the above.

Copyright © 2006 Pearson Education, Inc. Duplication for classroom use is permitted.

## Using Visuals

Look at the diagram. Choose the best answer. Circle the letter.

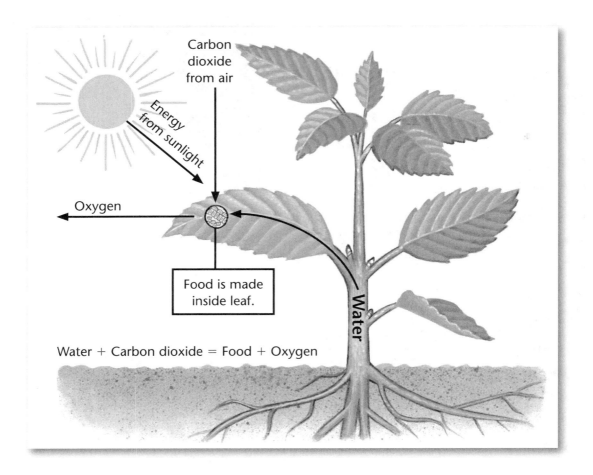

Carbon dioxide from air

Energy from sunlight

Oxygen

Food is made inside leaf.

Water

Water + Carbon dioxide = Food + Oxygen

**19.** What does this diagram show?

   **a.** Pollination

   **b.** Photosynthesis

   **c.** Germination

   **d.** The plant life cycle

**20.** What does the plant need to make food?

   **a.** Water

   **b.** Energy from sunlight

   **c.** Carbon dioxide from the air

   **d.** All of the above

**21.** What does the plant let out into the air during this process?

   **a.** Food

   **b.** Oxygen

   **c.** Carbon dioxide

   **d.** Energy from sunlight

## Writing

Write a paragraph about photosynthesis. Use the diagram above to help. Include how photosynthesis helps animals. Make sure your paragraph has a beginning, a middle, and an end.

Copyright © 2006 Pearson Education, Inc. Duplication for classroom use is permitted

# Unit 2: Lesson 1 Test

## Key Words

Choose the best answer. Circle the letter.

1. All animals need oxygen, water, food, and shelter to _____.
   a. have adaptations
   b. have fur
   c. have traits
   d. survive

2. The shape of a bird's beak is _____.
   a. short
   b. a shelter
   c. a trait
   d. very long

3. An elephant and a bear are two different _____.
   a. traits
   b. species
   c. adaptations
   d. carnivores

4. Animals that eat both plants and other animals are _____.
   a. herbivores
   b. carnivores
   c. omnivores
   d. elephants and beavers

## Using Visuals

Look at the photograph. Choose the **true** sentence.
Circle the letter.

5. a. The horse is a carnivore.
   b. The horse is an herbivore.
   c. The horse is an omnivore.
   d. The horse is eating tarantulas.

Copyright © 2006 Pearson Education, Inc. Duplication for classroom use is permitted.

## Content

Choose the best answer. Circle the letter.

6. How are animals different from plants?

   a. Animals cannot make food the way plants do.

   b. Animals have to go from place to place to find food.

   c. Animals can move to get away from danger.

   d. All of the above.

7. How do fish get oxygen?

   a. They get oxygen by drinking.

   b. They breathe with their gills.

   c. They have to come to the top of the water.

   d. They get oxygen from the food they eat.

8. What is an animal shelter?

   a. An animal's home

   b. The color of an animal's hair

   c. The shape of an animal's teeth

   d. None of the above

9. What are adaptations?

   a. Adaptations are animals.

   b. Adaptations are things you find in the ground.

   c. Adaptations are traits that help an animal survive.

   d. Adaptations are plants.

10. Look at the picture. What adaptation do carnivores have?

    a. Flat teeth

    b. Sharp teeth

    c. Fur or hair

    d. None of the above

11. What is an example of a human trait?

    a. Eye color

    b. Hair color

    c. Both sharp and flat teeth

    d. All of the above

## Writing

Write a paragraph about animals and their traits. Make sure your paragraph has a beginning, a middle, and an end.

Copyright © 2006 Pearson Education, Inc. Duplication for classroom use is permitted.

Copyright © 2006 Pearson Education, Inc. Duplication for classroom use is permitted.

# Unit 2: Lesson 2 Test

## Key Words

Choose the best answer. Circle the letter.

1. Animals with backbones are _____.
   - **a.** jellyfish
   - **b.** butterflies
   - **c.** vertebrates
   - **d.** invertebrates

2. Humans and cows are both _____.
   - **a.** invertebrates
   - **b.** reptiles
   - **c.** amphibians
   - **d.** mammals

3. Lizards and turtles are both _____.
   - **a.** amphibians
   - **b.** mammals
   - **c.** reptiles
   - **d.** invertebrates

4. Animals use their bodies and sounds to _____.
   - **a.** communicate
   - **b.** sleep
   - **c.** grow
   - **d.** move

## Using Visuals

Look at the pie chart. Choose the **true** sentence. Circle the letter.

5. **a.** Five percent are invertebrates.
   - **b.** Ninety-five percent are vertebrates.
   - **c.** There are more vertebrate species.
   - **d.** There are more invertebrate species.

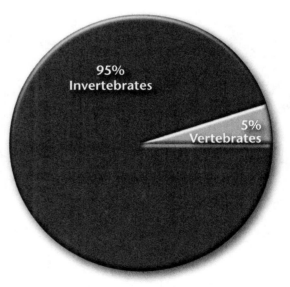

**The Animal Kingdom**

95% Invertebrates

5% Vertebrates

## Content

Choose the best answer. Circle the letter.

**6.** How do fish move?

   **a.** They use sound.

   **b.** They use their fins.

   **c.** They use their gills.

   **d.** They use their lungs.

**7.** Look at the picture. What kind of animal is this?

   **a.** A fish

   **b.** A reptile

   **c.** A mammal

   **d.** An amphibian

**8.** Look at the picture. What is **not** true about this group?

   **a.** They hatch from eggs.

   **b.** They have gills, then lungs.

   **c.** They grow wings when they are older.

   **d.** They live in water first, later on land.

**9.** What is true about **all** reptiles?

   **a.** They have gills.

   **b.** They have scales or plates.

   **c.** They live in the ocean.

   **d.** They have no backbones.

**10.** Where do birds, amphibians, and most fish and reptiles come from?

   **a.** They hatch from eggs.

   **b.** Their mothers give live birth.

   **c.** They come from a hole on the beach.

   **d.** None of the above.

**11.** What is true about **all** mammals?

   **a.** They have lungs.

   **b.** They give birth to live young.

   **c.** They have fur or hair.

   **d.** All of the above.

## Writing

Write a paragraph about vertebrates and invertebrates. Include key facts about both groups. Give examples of animals in each group. Make sure your paragraph has a beginning, a middle, and an end.

Copyright © 2006 Pearson Education, Inc. Duplication for classroom use is permitted

# Unit 2: Unit Test

## Key Words

Choose the best answer. Circle the letter.

1. The two main groups of animals are _____.
   a. herbivores and mammals
   b. vertebrates and invertebrates
   c. carnivores and vertebrates
   d. omnivores and reptiles

2. A backbone is a trait of all _____.
   a. vertebrates
   b. invertebrates
   c. arthropods
   d. species

3. Look at the picture. This animal is _____.
   a. an amphibian
   b. a reptile
   c. an invertebrate
   d. a vertebrate

4. Sharp teeth and flat teeth are adaptations of all _____.
   a. crabs
   b. carnivores
   c. herbivores
   d. omnivores

5. Scales or hard plates are traits of _____.
   a. reptiles
   b. elephants
   c. mammals
   d. amphibians

6. Animals with large, flat teeth are _____.
   a. lions
   b. herbivores
   c. omnivores
   d. carnivores

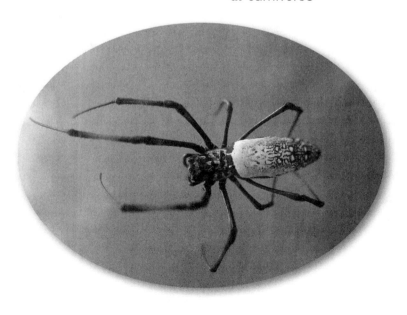

Copyright © 2006 Pearson Education, Inc. Duplication for classroom use is permitted.

## Content

Choose the best answer. Circle the letter.

7. What do animals need to survive?

   **a.** Food and water

   **b.** Oxygen

   **c.** Shelter

   **d.** All of the above

8. Which animal is **not** an herbivore?

   **a.** A horse

   **b.** A cow

   **c.** A lion

   **d.** A beaver

9. What is an example of a carnivore?

   **a.** A wolf

   **b.** A lion

   **c.** A praying mantis

   **d.** All of the above

10. Look at the picture. What kind of animals are these?

    **a.** Mammals

    **b.** Fish

    **c.** Reptiles

    **d.** Amphibians

11. Which sentence is **not** true about the animals in the picture?

    **a.** They hatch from eggs.

    **b.** They have lungs.

    **c.** They have fur or hair.

    **d.** They have scales.

12. Which sentence is true of **all** amphibians?

    **a.** Amphibians are invertebrates.

    **b.** Amphibians have gills first and lungs later.

    **c.** Amphibians lay eggs on land.

    **d.** Amphibians give milk to their young.

Copyright © 2006 Pearson Education, Inc. Duplication for classroom use is permitted.

**13.** Look at the picture. Which sentence is **not** true about this animal?

    **a.** It has wings.

    **b.** It can fly.

    **c.** It has feathers.

    **d.** It hatched from an egg.

**14.** What do humans and whales have in common?

    **a.** They are both mammals.

    **b.** They are both vertebrates.

    **c.** They both feed milk to their young.

    **d.** All of the above.

**15.** What is **not** a trait of **all** fish?

    **a.** They have fins.

    **b.** They have gills.

    **c.** They have lungs.

    **d.** They live in water.

**16.** Which animals are invertebrates?

    **a.** Reptiles, fish, and amphibians

    **b.** Birds and mammals

    **c.** Jellyfish and crabs

    **d.** Dogs and cats

## Reading Strategies

Choose the best answer. Circle the letter.

**17.** How do you **use what you know**?

    **a.** Guess what you will learn about.

    **b.** Think about what you already know about a topic.

    **c.** Think about how things are the same and different.

    **d.** Ask your teacher questions.

**18.** What are **key sentences**?

    **a.** Sentences that come at the end of a paragraph.

    **b.** Sentences that compare and contrast two things.

    **c.** Sentences that tell you important facts about a topic.

    **d.** None of the above.

Copyright © 2006 Pearson Education, Inc. Duplication for classroom use is permitted.

Name _____ Date _____

## Using Visuals

Look at the pie charts. Choose the best answer. Circle the letter.

**Mammals**

25%
Endangered

**Birds**

11%
Endangered

**Fish**

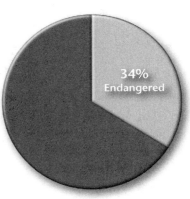

34%
Endangered

**19.** What do these pie charts show?

   **a.** The percent of invertebrates

   **b.** The percent of traits in each group

   **c.** The percent of adaptations in each group

   **d.** The percent of endangered species in each group

**20.** What percent of mammal and bird species are endangered?

   **a.** 25% of mammal species and 11% of bird species

   **b.** 11% of mammal species and 34% of bird species

   **c.** 75% of mammal species and 89% of bird species

   **d.** 100% of both species

**21.** What percent of fish species are **not** endangered?

   **a.** 25%

   **b.** 34%

   **c.** 66%

   **d.** 100%

## Writing

Choose **one** vertebrate group to write about (mammals, reptiles, fish, birds, or amphibians). Write a paragraph about the key facts and traits of this group. Give one or more examples of animals in the group. Make sure your paragraph has a beginning, a middle, and an end.

Copyright © 2006 Pearson Education, Inc. Duplication for classroom use is permitted

# Unit 3: Lesson 1 Test

## Key Words

Choose the best answer. Circle the letter.

1. All rocks are made of _____.
   - **a.** copper
   - **b.** marble
   - **c.** minerals
   - **d.** fossils

2. Hot liquid rock from a volcano makes _____.
   - **a.** fossils
   - **b.** igneous rock
   - **c.** sedimentary rock
   - **d.** metamorphic rock

3. Sand, mud, and tiny pieces of rock join to make _____.
   - **a.** copper
   - **b.** metamorphic rock
   - **c.** igneous rock
   - **d.** sedimentary rock

4. Heat and pressure deep underground can create _____.
   - **a.** igneous rock
   - **b.** sedimentary rock
   - **c.** metamorphic rock
   - **d.** fossils

## Using Visuals

Look at the sectional diagram. Choose the best answer. Circle the letter.

5. What is the earth's crust made of?
   - **a.** Solid metal
   - **b.** Soft rock
   - **c.** Solid rock
   - **d.** Liquid metal

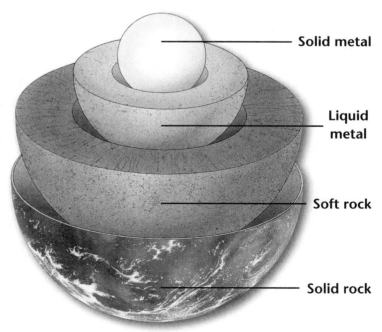

Solid metal

Liquid metal

Soft rock

Solid rock

Copyright © 2006 Pearson Education, Inc. Duplication for classroom use is permitted.

**Content**

Choose the best answer. Circle the letter.

6. What is solid, has crystals, and happens naturally?

   a. A mineral

   b. Halite

   c. Copper

   d. All of the above

7. What is **not** a property of a diamond?

   a. It makes good wire.

   b. You can see through it.

   c. It shines when it is cut.

   d. It's the hardest mineral.

8. What are two types of igneous rock?

   a. Marble and slate

   b. Extrusive and intrusive

   c. Sedimentary and metamorphic

   d. Salt and diamonds

9. What can you often find in sedimentary rock?

   a. Pumice

   b. Diamonds

   c. Fossils

   d. None of the above

10. Look at the picture. What is this building made of?

    a. Metamorphic rock

    b. Sedimentary rock

    c. Igneous rock

    d. Pumice

11. What can igneous rock change into?

    a. Sedimentary rock

    b. Hot liquid rock

    c. Metamorphic rock

    d. All of the above

**Writing**

Write a paragraph about **one** type of rock (igneous, sedimentary, or metamorphic). Include how it is formed. Make sure your paragraph has a beginning, a middle, and an end.

Copyright © 2006 Pearson Education, Inc. Duplication for classroom use is permitted

# Unit 3: Lesson 2 Test

Copyright © 2006 Pearson Education, Inc. Duplication for classroom use is permitted.

## Key Words

Choose the best answer. Circle the letter.

1. A scientist who studies rocks is a _____.
   a. glacier
   b. botanist
   c. geologist
   d. geology

2. Rocks break into small pieces in a process called _____.
   a. geology
   b. weathering
   c. erosion
   d. rounded rock

3. Wind, water, and ice move rocks in a process called _____.
   a. earthquake
   b. geology
   c. erosion
   d. weathering

4. Pressure causes the earth's crust to move during _____.
   a. an earthquake
   b. a glacier
   c. a geologist
   d. erosion

## Using Visuals

Look at the photo sequence of Mount St. Helens. Choose the **true** sentence. Circle the letter.

5. a. Mount St. Helens was not active.
   b. Mount St. Helens caused an earthquake.
   c. Mount St. Helens caused a tsunami.
   d. Mount St. Helens looked very different after the eruption.

## Content

Choose the best answer. Circle the letter.

**6.** What causes weathering?

   **a.** Wind, rain, and ice

   **b.** Plants and animals

   **c.** Saltwater, waves, and sand

   **d.** All of the above

**7.** How does a glacier move rocks?

   **a.** It picks up rocks as it goes down a mountain.

   **b.** It blows rocks a long way.

   **c.** It causes the earth to shake.

   **d.** All of the above.

**8.** How can water break rock?

   **a.** Water can freeze in a crack.

   **b.** Waves can crash into a rock.

   **c.** Rain and saltwater can make rocks weak.

   **d.** All of the above.

**9.** Look at the picture. Where do earthquakes often happen?

   **a.** Near glaciers

   **b.** Near faults

   **c.** Near weathering

   **d.** Near farms

**10.** What is a tsunami?

   **a.** A deep hole in the earth

   **b.** A large sheet of ice on a mountain

   **c.** A dangerous wave caused by an earthquake

   **d.** Sand blown by the wind

**11.** Why do most volcanoes have a mountain of rock around them?

   **a.** Weathering caused hillsides to form.

   **b.** Wind caused rock to build up.

   **c.** Liquid rock from eruptions became hard.

   **d.** All mountains are volcanoes.

## Writing

Write a paragraph about earthquakes, tsunami, **or** volcanoes. Include the cause. Make sure your paragraph has a beginning, a middle, and an end.

Copyright © 2006 Pearson Education, Inc. Duplication for classroom use is permitted

# Unit 3: Unit Test

## Key Words

Choose the best answer. Circle the letter.

1. The study of rocks is called _____.

    **a.** geology

    **b.** life science

    **c.** physical science

    **d.** geologist

2. Pressure changes layers of sand, mud, and rock into _____.

    **a.** hot liquid rock

    **b.** metamorphic rock

    **c.** sedimentary rock

    **d.** igneous rock

3. Clear and very hard are two _____ of diamond crystals.

    **a.** minerals

    **b.** properties

    **c.** fossils

    **d.** glaciers

4. Tsunami are caused by _____.

    **a.** minerals

    **b.** glaciers

    **c.** earthquakes

    **d.** weathered rocks

5. Look at the picture. This is _____.

    **a.** the hardest mineral

    **b.** igneous rock

    **c.** sedimentary rock

    **d.** metamorphic rock

6. Large sheets of ice on a mountain are called _____.

    **a.** glaciers

    **b.** volcanoes

    **c.** tsunami

    **d.** earthquakes

Copyright © 2006 Pearson Education, Inc. Duplication for classroom use is permitted.

## Content

Choose the best answer. Circle the letter.

**7.** Look at the picture. What is this?

 **a.** A mineral

 **b.** Halite

 **c.** Salt

 **d.** All of the above

**8.** What are the three properties of a mineral?

 **a.** It is soft, has layers, and is made by people.

 **b.** It is solid, gray, and made underground.

 **c.** It is solid, has crystals, and happens naturally.

 **d.** It is soft, it shines, and you can see through it.

**9.** How many kinds of minerals make up most of the earth's rocks?

 **a.** Only one

 **b.** About 20

 **c.** About 500,000

 **d.** About 1,000,000

**10.** How is metamorphic rock formed?

 **a.** By a volcano

 **b.** By weathering

 **c.** By a tsunami

 **d.** By heat and pressure deep underground

**11.** What is the rock life cycle?

 **a.** Rocks can change from one type to another.

 **b.** Rocks live and die like plants or animals.

 **c.** A volcano erupts, and then stops.

 **d.** None of the above.

**12.** What is weathering?

 **a.** Heated rock becomes hot liquid rock.

 **b.** Weather, plants, and animals weaken and break rock.

 **c.** Pressure forms layers of sedimentary rock.

 **d.** All of the above.

Copyright © 2006 Pearson Education, Inc. Duplication for classroom use is permitted.

**13.** What is erosion?

  **a.** Glaciers move pieces of rock.

  **b.** The wind moves rocks and sand.

  **c.** Water and rain move rocks.

  **d.** All of the above.

**14.** What are the four layers of the earth?

  **a.** Ice, water, soil, and rock

  **b.** The surface, the metal, the minerals, and the inner parts

  **c.** The crust, the mantle, the outer core, and the inner core

  **d.** The sedimentary, igneous, metamorphic, and hot liquid rock

**15.** What causes earthquakes?

  **a.** Erosion causes cracks in the earth.

  **b.** They are caused by dangerous waves.

  **c.** They are caused by volcanoes.

  **d.** Pressure causes pieces of the earth's crust to move.

**16.** Look at the picture. What happened to the rock?

  **a.** A volcano changed its shape.

  **b.** Water changed its shape.

  **c.** Sand changed its shape.

  **d.** None of the above.

## Reading Strategies

Choose the best answer. Circle the letter.

**17.** How can **asking questions** help you?

  **a.** It can help you sound out words.

  **b.** It can help you learn spelling.

  **c.** It can help you understand what you read.

  **d.** None of the above.

**18.** How do you understand **cause and effect**?

  **a.** Look for what makes something happen.

  **b.** Look for what happens.

  **c.** Look for words like *caused* and *because of*.

  **d.** All of the above.

## Using Visuals

Look at the sectional diagram. Choose the best answer. Circle the letter.

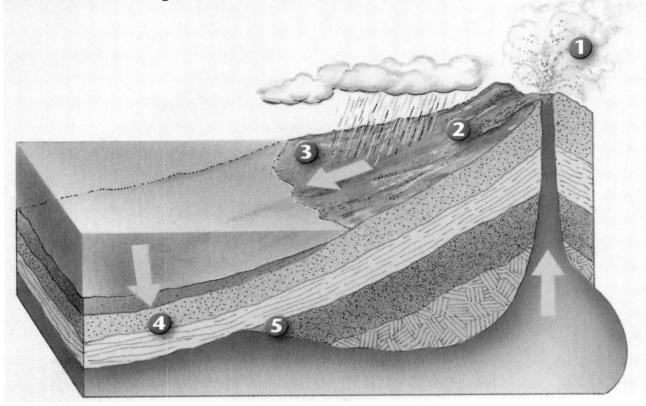

**19.** Number _____ shows the weathering and erosion of rock.

  **a.** 1

  **b.** 3

  **c.** 5

  **d.** None of the above

**20.** Number _____ shows pressure creating sedimentary rock.

  **a.** 1

  **b.** 2

  **c.** 4

  **d.** None of the above

**21.** Number _____ shows the melting of sedimentary and metamorphic rock.

  **a.** 2

  **b.** 3

  **c.** 5

  **d.** None of the above

## Writing

Write a paragraph about the rock cycle. Use the diagram above for help. Describe how different types of rock are formed and how they change. Make sure your paragraph has a beginning, a middle, and an end.

# Unit 4: Lesson 1 Test

## Key Words

Choose the best answer. Circle the letter.

**1.** Earth is part of the Milky Way _____.

   **a.** galaxy

   **b.** solar system

   **c.** orbit

   **d.** atmosphere

**2.** The sun is at the center of our _____.

   **a.** Milky Way

   **b.** atmosphere

   **c.** solar system

   **d.** galaxy

**3.** Earth and eight other planets _____ the sun.

   **a.** hit

   **b.** orbit

   **c.** travel away from

   **d.** have an atmosphere like

**4.** Oxygen and other gases make up Earth's _____.

   **a.** asteroids

   **b.** craters

   **c.** atmosphere

   **d.** poisonous gases

## Using Visuals

Look at the illustration. Choose the best answer. Circle the letter.

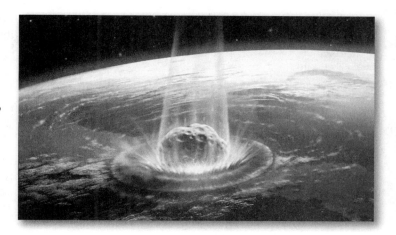

**5.** What event does this illustration show?

   **a.** An asteroid hit Earth long ago.

   **b.** A comet hit the sun long ago.

   **c.** The moon hit Earth long ago.

   **d.** A rover hit Earth long ago.

Copyright © 2006 Pearson Education, Inc. Duplication for classroom use is permitted.

## Content

Choose the best answer. Circle the letter.

6. What are Mercury, Venus, Earth, and Mars mostly made of?

    a. Gases

    b. Water

    c. Ice

    d. Rock

7. Why are Mercury, Venus, Earth, and Mars called the inner planets?

    a. They move around a moon.

    b. They are closer to the sun.

    c. They are far from the sun.

    d. Mercury, Venus, and Mars are close to Earth.

8. What is **not** true about Mercury?

    a. It has water.

    b. It is hot and dry.

    c. It is small.

    d. It is closest to the sun.

9. What is Mars often called?

    a. The blue planet

    b. The red planet

    c. The largest planet

    d. The smallest planet

10. What is **not** true about Jupiter, Saturn, Uranus, Neptune, and Pluto?

    a. They are called the outer planets.

    b. They are mostly made of gases.

    c. They are close to the sun.

    d. They are very cold.

11. Look at the picture. What is this?

    a. An asteroid

    b. A galaxy

    c. A crater

    d. A comet

## Writing

Write a paragraph about our solar system. Include information about the inner and outer planets. Make sure your paragraph has a beginning, a middle, and an end.

Copyright © 2006 Pearson Education, Inc. Duplication for classroom use is permitted.

Name _____ Date _____

# Unit 4: Lesson 2 Test

## Key Words

Choose the best answer. Circle the letter.

1. _____ is everything in space, including planets, stars, and galaxies.

   **a.** An astronomer

   **b.** A constellation

   **c.** A telescope

   **d.** The universe

2. Stars make a pattern in the Ursa Major _____.

   **a.** constellation

   **b.** astronomer

   **c.** telescope

   **d.** trillion

3. _____ use telescopes to study objects in space.

   **a.** Botanists

   **b.** Geologists

   **c.** Astronomers

   **d.** Constellations

4. 1,000,000,000,000 is _____.

   **a.** a hundred thousand

   **b.** a million

   **c.** a billion

   **d.** a trillion

## Using Visuals

Look at the deep space photo. Choose the best answer. Circle the letter.

5. What does this deep space photo show?

   **a.** All of the universe

   **b.** Spiral and elliptical galaxies

   **c.** Our solar system

   **d.** A trillion galaxies

## Content

Choose the best answer. Circle the letter.

**6.** How many stars are there in the universe?

   **a.** Perhaps a million

   **b.** Perhaps a billion

   **c.** Perhaps a trillion

   **d.** Perhaps a trillion trillion

**7.** Why don't you see many stars during the day?

   **a.** They only come out at night.

   **b.** The sun is too bright.

   **c.** They are behind Earth during the day.

   **d.** All of the above.

**8.** What is Sirius?

   **a.** The brightest star in the night sky

   **b.** A large star

   **c.** A very hot blue-white star

   **d.** All of the above

**9.** Which color stars are the coolest?

   **a.** Blue stars

   **b.** White stars

   **c.** Yellow stars

   **d.** Red stars

**10.** What kind of star is the sun?

   **a.** A giant very hot star

   **b.** A small very hot star

   **c.** A medium-sized, medium-hot star

   **d.** A large cool star

**11.** Look at the picture. What is this?

   **a.** A new star

   **b.** A middle-aged star

   **c.** A dying star

   **d.** None of the above

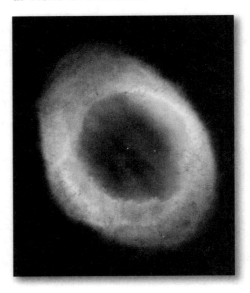

## Writing

Write a paragraph about stars. Include information about the sun. Make sure your paragraph has a beginning, a middle, and an end.

Copyright © 2006 Pearson Education, Inc. Duplication for classroom use is permitted.

# Unit 4: Unit Test

## Key Words

Choose the best answer. Circle the letter.

**1.** There are perhaps a trillion trillion stars in the _____.

  **a.** solar system

  **b.** Milky Way galaxy

  **c.** universe

  **d.** constellation Orion

**2.** Look at the picture. It shows billions of stars in our _____.

  **a.** Milky Way galaxy

  **b.** universe

  **c.** constellation Ursa Major

  **d.** solar system

**3.** Nine planets orbit the sun in our _____.

  **a.** constellation Scorpio

  **b.** Milky Way galaxy

  **c.** universe

  **d.** solar system

**4.** Animals can live on Earth because it has oxygen in its _____.

  **a.** craters

  **b.** asteroids

  **c.** atmosphere

  **d.** orbit

**5.** Near the sun, _____ turns into a cloud of gases with a long tail.

  **a.** an orbit

  **b.** a comet

  **c.** an asteroid

  **d.** a windstorm

**6.** The Hubble Space Telescope was named for _____.

  **a.** a star

  **b.** a planet

  **c.** a constellation

  **d.** an astronomer

**Content**

Choose the best answer. Circle the letter.

**7.** What planets are the inner planets?

    **a.** Saturn, Mars, and Pluto

    **b.** Jupiter, Saturn, Uranus, Neptune, and Pluto

    **c.** Mercury, Venus, Earth, and Mars

    **d.** Venus, Earth, Saturn, and Uranus

**8.** What is **not** true about the inner planets?

    **a.** They are closer to the sun.

    **b.** They all have liquid water.

    **c.** They are made mostly of rock.

    **d.** They are smaller than most of the outer planets.

**9.** Which planet is closest to the sun?

    **a.** Mercury

    **b.** Jupiter

    **c.** Pluto

    **d.** Mars

**10.** Look at the picture. What are these?

    **a.** Planets

    **b.** Asteroids

    **c.** Galaxies

    **d.** Comets

**11.** What planets are the outer planets?

    **a.** Mercury, Venus, Earth, and Mars

    **b.** Saturn, Mars, and Pluto

    **c.** Saturn, Uranus, Earth, and Venus

    **d.** Jupiter, Saturn, Uranus, Neptune, and Pluto

**12.** What's **not** true about the outer planets?

    **a.** They are mostly made of gases.

    **b.** They are far from the sun.

    **c.** Most are very large.

    **d.** They are very hot.

**13.** Which planet has big rings that are easy to see?

    **a.** Mars

    **b.** Saturn

    **c.** Pluto

    **d.** Mercury

**14.** What is **not** true about Pluto?

    **a.** It is made of rock and ice.

    **b.** It is farthest from the sun.

    **c.** It is the largest planet in the solar system.

    **d.** It is the coldest planet in the solar system.

**15.** Look at the picture. What is this?

    **a.** The Big Dipper

    **b.** The Great Bear

    **c.** The constellation Orion

    **d.** The constellation Leo the Lion

**16.** Which color stars are the hottest?

    **a.** Blue

    **b.** Red

    **c.** Orange

    **d.** Yellow

## Reading Strategies

Choose the best answer. Circle the letter.

**17.** Why do you **reread** a difficult paragraph?

    **a.** To preview

    **b.** To understand more details

    **c.** To look at the pictures

    **d.** All of the above

**18.** How do you **visualize**?

    **a.** Look for the key words.

    **b.** Compare and contrast two things.

    **c.** Make pictures of the words in your mind.

    **d.** All of the above.

Copyright © 2006 Pearson Education, Inc. Duplication for classroom use is permitted.

Name _____ Date _____

## Using Visuals

Look at the photos. Choose the best answer. Circle the letter.

 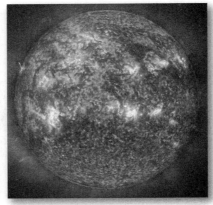 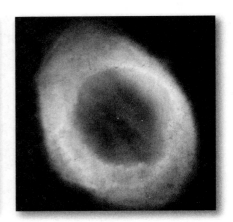

19. What do these photos show?

    a. The star life cycle

    b. Elliptical galaxies

    c. The Milky Way

    d. Spiral galaxies

20. What does the first photo show?

    a. A star begins as a ring.

    b. Spiral galaxies are oval.

    c. Elliptical galaxies are oval.

    d. A star begins as a cloud of gases and dust.

21. What kind of star is the sun?

    a. A new star

    b. A middle-aged star

    c. A dying star

    d. None of the above

## Writing

Write a paragraph about what the universe contains. Include information about where our planet is in the universe. Make sure your paragraph has a beginning, a middle, and an end.

Copyright © 2006 Pearson Education, Inc. Duplication for classroom use is permitted.

Name _____ Date _____

# Unit 5: Lesson 1 Test

## Key Words

Choose the best answer. Circle the letter.

1. This test and everything around you _____.
   a. is matter
   b. has mass and volume
   c. has density
   d. All of the above

2. _____ is the amount of space something takes up.
   a. Mass
   b. Matter
   c. Volume
   d. Density

3. You can use a balance to measure _____ in grams and kilograms.
   a. volume
   b. mass
   c. taste
   d. All of the above

4. Everything is made up of very tiny pieces called _____.
   a. dots
   b. atoms
   c. density
   d. the metric system

## Using Visuals

Look at the picture. Choose the best answer. Circle the letter.

5. How can you see atoms?
   a. With your eyes
   b. With a hand lens
   c. In a micrograph
   d. With a telescope

Copyright © 2006 Pearson Education, Inc. Duplication for classroom use is permitted.

Name _____    Date _____

## Content

Choose the best answer. Circle the letter.

6. How can you use your senses to learn about properties of matter?

   a. You can look at something.

   b. You can feel something.

   c. You can taste something.

   d. All of the above.

7. What is **not** a property of wood?

   a. It is sweet and sticky.

   b. It usually floats on water.

   c. It burns easily.

   d. It is hard.

8. How can you measure the volume of matter?

   a. With a balance

   b. With a ruler

   c. In a container

   d. With a microscope

9. Look at the picture. What does it show?

   a. Pennies and puffed rice have the same density.

   b. Pennies have a greater density than puffed rice.

   c. Puffed rice has a greater density than pennies.

   d. None of the above.

10. What is **true** about density?

   a. Mass and volume help you measure density.

   b. Density is how much gas something has per unit of volume.

   c. A liter of air has greater density than a liter of water.

   d. None of the above.

11. Which substance is a mixture of different kinds of matter?

   a. Sugar

   b. Salad

   c. Water

   d. Salt

## Writing

Write a paragraph about matter. Include information about its properties (including volume, mass, and density). Make sure your paragraph has a beginning, a middle, and an end.

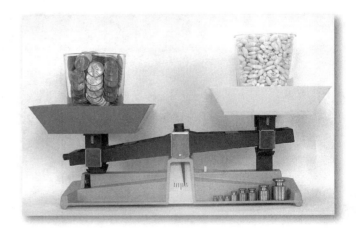

Copyright © 2006 Pearson Education, Inc. Duplication for classroom use is permitted.

# Unit 5: Lesson 2 Test

## Key Words

Choose the best answer. Circle the letter.

1. Solid, liquid, and gas are three _____ of matter.
   a. containers
   b. states
   c. chemicals
   d. substances

2. The temperature at which a solid changes to a liquid is its _____ point.
   a. state
   b. boiling
   c. melting
   d. chemical

3. The temperature at which a liquid changes to a gas is its _____ point.
   a. melting
   b. physical
   c. chemical
   d. boiling

4. The atoms of a substance change in a _____.
   a. chemical change
   b. physical change
   c. melting change
   d. boiling change

## Using Visuals

Look at the illustration. Choose the best answer. Circle the letter.

5. Which state of matter does this show?
   a. Solid
   b. Liquid
   c. Gas
   d. All of the above

Copyright © 2006 Pearson Education, Inc. Duplication for classroom use is permitted.

## Content

Choose the best answer. Circle the letter.

6. What is **not** true about a solid?

   a. It has a set shape.

   b. It has a set volume.

   c. It takes the shape of its container.

   d. Its atoms are very close together.

7. What is **not** true about a liquid?

   a. It has no set shape.

   b. It has a set volume.

   c. It takes the shape of its container.

   d. It can't change into a gas.

8. What is **not** true about a gas?

   a. It has a set shape and volume.

   b. It has no set shape or volume.

   c. It expands to fill any container.

   d. Its atoms move fast and are far apart.

9. What is **true** about boiling and melting points?

   a. All substances melt at 0° and boil at 100° Celsius.

   b. Each substance has its own boiling and melting point.

   c. The melting and boiling points of all matter are 50° Celsius.

   d. None of the above.

10. What happens when the temperature of water is higher than 100° Celsius?

    a. Water changes into a gas.

    b. Water makes a physical change.

    c. Water changes state, but its atoms remain the same.

    d. All of the above.

11. Look at the picture. What will happen to the food?

    a. A physical change

    b. A chemical change

    c. No change

    d. None of the above

## Writing

Wrte a paragraph about the three states of matter. Include information about each state. Make sure your paragraph has a beginning, a middle, and an end.

Copyright © 2006 Pearson Education, Inc. Duplication for classroom use is permitted.

# Unit 5: Unit Test

## Key Words

Choose the best answer. Circle the letter.

1. Anything that takes up space and has mass is _____.

   **a.** a solid

   **b.** matter

   **c.** a liquid

   **d.** a mixture

2. You can measure _____ with a balance.

   **a.** mass

   **b.** volume

   **c.** the melting point

   **d.** the boiling point

3. You can measure _____ with a container.

   **a.** the boiling point

   **b.** the melting point

   **c.** volume

   **d.** mass

4. Mass divided by volume equals _____.

   **a.** state

   **b.** chemicals

   **c.** matter

   **d.** density

5. Look at the picture. It shows two _____ of water.

   **a.** atoms

   **b.** chemicals

   **c.** states

   **d.** containers

6. A substance's melting point and boiling point are two of its _____.

   **a.** properties

   **b.** units

   **c.** atoms

   **d.** chemical changes

Copyright © 2006 Pearson Education, Inc. Duplication for classroom use is permitted.

## Content

Choose the best answer. Circle the letter.

7. What is **not** a property of water?

   **a.** Its boiling point is 100° Celsius.

   **b.** Its melting point is 0° Celsius.

   **c.** It tastes sour.

   **d.** It is clear.

8. What is ice melting an example of?

   **a.** A chemical change

   **b.** A physical change

   **c.** A change of atoms

   **d.** None of the above

9. What has a set shape and a set volume?

   **a.** A solid

   **b.** A liquid

   **c.** A gas

   **d.** Honey

10. What has a set volume, but no set shape?

    **a.** A solid

    **b.** A liquid

    **c.** A gas

    **d.** Wood

11. What has no set shape or set volume?

    **a.** A solid

    **b.** A liquid

    **c.** A gas

    **d.** Water

12. Look at the micrograph. What does it show?

    **a.** Sugar

    **b.** Atoms

    **c.** Salt

    **d.** A snowflake

Copyright © 2006 Pearson Education, Inc. Duplication for classroom use is permitted.

**13.** About how many atoms fit on the head of a pin?

    **a.** About 5

    **b.** About 5 million

    **c.** About a trillion trillion

    **d.** None of the above

**14.** Look at the picture of the rusting ship. What does it show?

    **a.** Stainless steel

    **b.** A physical change

    **c.** A chemical change

    **d.** The melting point of iron

**15.** What happens in a chemical change?

    **a.** The atoms change.

    **b.** The atoms stay the same.

    **c.** The atoms become larger.

    **d.** The atoms become smaller.

**16.** What kind of matter are you?

    **a.** I'm a pure substance.

    **b.** I'm a mixture.

    **c.** I'm a gas.

    **d.** I'm a liquid.

## Reading Strategies

Choose the best answer. Circle the letter.

**17.** How do you look for **facts and examples**?

    **a.** Look for the main science points, or facts.

    **b.** Look for examples that help you understand the facts.

    **c.** Look for words like *for example* and *suppose*.

    **d.** All of the above.

**18.** What is an **idea map**?

    **a.** It is a word map. You make it to connect important ideas in a text.

    **b.** It is a drawing of an experiment.

    **c.** It shows a city or state.

    **d.** All of the above.

Copyright © 2006 Pearson Education, Inc. Duplication for classroom use is permitted.

Name _____ Date _____

## Using Visuals

Look at the states of matter illustration. Choose the best answer. Circle the letter.

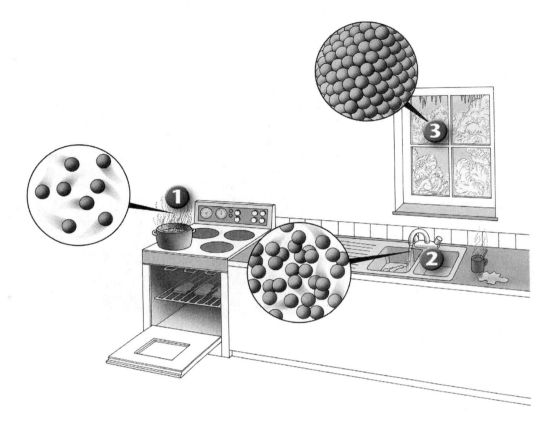

**19.** What is **true** about water as shown in number 1?

    **a.** The water's atoms are moving very slowly.

    **b.** Water is changing from a liquid to a gas.

    **c.** The water's atoms are close together.

    **d.** The temperature is lower than 100° Celsius.

**20.** What is **true** about water as shown in number 2?

    **a.** Water is a solid.

    **b.** The water's atoms are very close together.

    **c.** The water's atoms are not moving around.

    **d.** The temperature is higher than 0° Celsius.

**21.** What is **true** about water as shown in number 3?

    **a.** Water is a liquid.

    **b.** The water's atoms are very close together.

    **c.** The water's atoms are moving very fast.

    **d.** The temperature is higher than 0° Celsius.

## Writing

Write a paragraph about how water changes states. Include information about the atoms in each state. Use the diagram above to help. Make sure your paragraph has a beginning, a middle, and an end.

Copyright © 2006 Pearson Education, Inc. Duplication for classroom use is permitted.

# Unit 6: Lesson 1 Test

## Key Words

Choose the best answer. Circle the letter.

**1.** Sound waves come from _____.
- **a.** pitch
- **b.** decibels
- **c.** volume
- **d.** vibrations

**2.** We hear sound when _____ make our eardrums vibrate.
- **a.** circles
- **b.** bounces
- **c.** sound waves
- **d.** hard surfaces

**3.** A loud shout is a high- _____ sound.
- **a.** echo
- **b.** volume
- **c.** vibration
- **d.** hertz

**4.** Sound waves bounce off hard surfaces to make _____.
- **a.** pitch
- **b.** echoes
- **c.** frequency
- **d.** hertz

## Using Visuals

Look at the chart. Choose the best answer. Circle the letter.

**5.** What does sound move fastest through?
- **a.** Solids
- **b.** Liquids
- **c.** Gases
- **d.** Air

| Matter | Speed of Sound (Meters Per Second) |
|---|---|
| Dry, cold air | 343 |
| Water | 1,550 |
| Hard wood | 3,960 |
| Steel | 5,050 |

Copyright © 2006 Pearson Education, Inc. Duplication for classroom use is permitted.

## Content

Choose the best answer. Circle the letter.

**6.** How do sound waves move?

   **a.** They move out in circles.

   **b.** They move out in all directions.

   **c.** They travel only through solids, liquids, and gases.

   **d.** All of the above.

**7.** Why don't you hear an echo in a room with a lot of soft things?

   **a.** The air absorbs the sound waves.

   **b.** Sound waves can't move inside a room.

   **c.** The soft things absorb the sound waves.

   **d.** The sound waves bounce off the soft things.

**8.** What is **true** about a high-volume sound?

   **a.** It sounds very soft.

   **b.** It has a lot of energy.

   **c.** It doesn't take a lot of energy to make it.

   **d.** All of the above.

**9.** Look at the picture. What is **not** true about this whistle sound?

   **a.** It has a high pitch.

   **b.** It makes the air vibrate quickly.

   **c.** It makes a low-frequency sound.

   **d.** The sound waves are close together.

**10.** How do we measure sound waves?

   **a.** We measure volume in decibels.

   **b.** We measure frequency in hertz.

   **c.** We measure speed in meters per second.

   **d.** All of the above.

**11.** Why does sound move slowly through gases?

   **a.** The atoms are far apart.

   **b.** The atoms are close together.

   **c.** Gases have a lot of water vapor.

   **d.** Sound can't travel through gases.

## Writing

Write a paragraph about how we hear sound. Include information about volume, pitch, and frequency. Make sure your paragraph has a beginning, a middle, and an end.

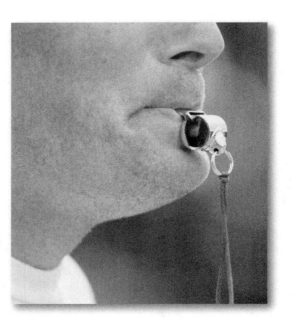

Copyright © 2006 Pearson Education, Inc. Duplication for classroom use is permitted

Copyright © 2006 Pearson Education, Inc. Duplication for classroom use is permitted.

Name _____ Date _____

# Unit 6: Lesson 2 Test

## Key Words

Choose the best answer. Circle the letter.

1. _____ waves have their own energy.
   a. Sound
   b. Opaque
   c. Translucent
   d. Electromagnetic

2. We can see clearly through _____ materials.
   a. opaque
   b. uneven
   c. transparent
   d. translucent

3. The moon, an apple, and a wall are all _____.
   a. prisms
   b. opaque
   c. transparent
   d. translucent

4. We can see the moon because it _____ the sun's light.
   a. refracts
   b. reflects
   c. absorbs
   d. makes

## Using Visuals

Look at the wave diagram. Choose the best answer. Circle the letter.

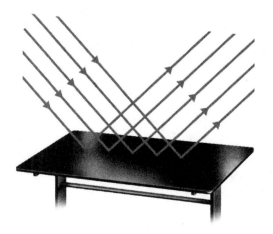

5. Why can you see yourself in a smooth surface?
   a. A smooth surface absorbs the light waves.
   b. The light waves pass through a smooth surface.
   c. The light waves bounce off at the same angle.
   d. The light waves bounce off at different angles.

## Content

Choose the best answer. Circle the letter.

6. Why can't we see most electromagnetic waves?

   a. Their frequencies are too low and their wavelengths are too long.

   b. Their frequencies are too high and their wavelengths are too short.

   c. They bounce off hard surfaces.

   d. Both a and b.

7. Why can we see through a transparent material?

   a. Light waves break off in different directions in it.

   b. Light waves pass through it.

   c. Light waves bounce off it.

   d. It absorbs light waves.

8. What causes the different colors of light?

   a. Different wavelengths and frequencies

   b. X rays and gamma rays

   c. Ultraviolet waves

   d. Both b and c

9. Why does a lemon look yellow?

   a. Because some light waves bounce off it

   b. Because it reflects the yellow wavelength

   c. Because it absorbs all the wavelengths except yellow

   d. All of the above

10. Look at the picture. What does it show?

    a. A prism

    b. The refraction of light

    c. The reflection of light

    d. Both a and b

11. How does a prism work?

    a. It refracts each wavelength of light at a different angle.

    b. It reflects each wavelength of light at the same angle.

    c. Light waves bounce off it in different directions.

    d. None of the above.

## Writing

Write a paragraph about how we can see things. Include information about how light is reflected and absorbed, and how we see colors. Make sure your paragraph has a beginning, a middle, and an end.

Copyright © 2006 Pearson Education, Inc. Duplication for classroom use is permitted

# Unit 6: Unit Test

## Key Words

Choose the best answer. Circle the letter.

1. _____ travel through the air in sound waves.

   **a.** Vibrations

   **b.** Reflections

   **c.** X rays

   **d.** Electromagnetic waves

2. _____ can only travel through solids, liquids, and gases.

   **a.** X rays

   **b.** Sound waves

   **c.** Radio waves

   **d.** Electromagnetic waves

3. We can't hear many of the high-_____ sounds mice make.

   **a.** echo

   **b.** volume

   **c.** frequency

   **d.** translucent

4. Light, X rays, and ultraviolet waves are all _____.

   **a.** visible light

   **b.** high-pitch sounds

   **c.** high-volume waves

   **d.** electromagnetic waves

5. Light bouncing off a surface is called _____.

   **a.** reflection

   **b.** refraction

   **c.** echoes

   **d.** vibration

6. Look at the picture. It shows _____.

   **a.** frequency

   **b.** reflection

   **c.** refraction

   **d.** sound waves

Copyright © 2006 Pearson Education, Inc. Duplication for classroom use is permitted.

**Content**

Choose the best answer. Circle the letter.

**7.** Where can you hear an echo?

   **a.** In a place with a lot of soft things

   **b.** In a place with a lot of hard surfaces

   **c.** In a living room with cushions and carpet

   **d.** All of the above

**8.** What kind of waves are close together?

   **a.** Low-volume waves

   **b.** Low-frequency waves

   **c.** High-volume waves

   **d.** High-frequency waves

**9.** What kind of sound does it take a lot of energy to make?

   **a.** A low pitch

   **b.** A high pitch

   **c.** A high-volume sound

   **d.** A low-volume sound

**10.** What kind of matter does sound move through most slowly?

   **a.** Solids

   **b.** Liquids

   **c.** Gases

   **d.** It travels at the same speed in all matter.

**11.** Why can you see this test you are taking?

   **a.** Light is reflecting off it.

   **b.** It is transparent.

   **c.** It is translucent.

   **d.** Light is refracting in it.

**12.** Look at the photograph. What is the glass?

   **a.** Transparent

   **b.** Translucent

   **c.** Opaque

   **d.** Liquid

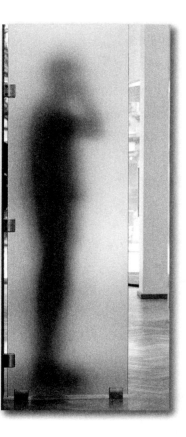

Copyright © 2006 Pearson Education, Inc. Duplication for classroom use is permitted.

**13.** Look at the picture. Why do we see a reflection?

    **a.** The smooth surface absorbs light.

    **b.** Light passes through the smooth surface.

    **c.** Light bounces off the smooth surface at the same angle.

    **d.** Light bounces off the smooth surface at different angles.

**14.** An object reflects blue and absorbs the other wavelengths of light. What color do you see?

    **a.** White

    **b.** Violet

    **c.** Blue

    **d.** All the colors except blue

**15.** What causes rainbows?

    **a.** Water droplets in the air refract light.

    **b.** Water droplets act like a prism.

    **c.** Water droplets separate the sunlight into its different wavelengths.

    **d.** All of the above.

**16.** What is **not** true about electromagnetic waves?

    **a.** They have their own energy.

    **b.** They all travel very fast at the same speed.

    **c.** They have different wavelengths and frequencies.

    **d.** We can see most electromagnetic waves.

## Reading Strategies

Choose the best answer. Circle the letter.

**17.** How do you **act it out**?

    **a.** Draw a picture or diagram.

    **b.** Use your body and objects around you.

    **c.** Look for words like *act* and *action*.

    **d.** Close your eyes and imagine a picture.

**18.** How can **drawing a picture** help you when you're reading?

    **a.** It can help you sound out words.

    **b.** It can help you understand difficult ideas.

    **c.** It can help you remember difficult ideas.

    **d.** Both b and c.

Copyright © 2006 Pearson Education, Inc. Duplication for classroom use is permitted.

Name _____  Date _____

Look at the electromagnetic wave diagram. Choose the best answer. Circle the letter.

## Electromagnetic Spectrum

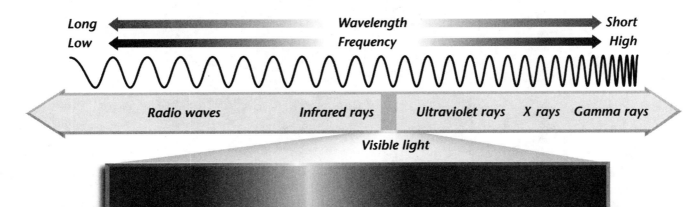

**19.** What is the only kind of electromagnetic wave we can see?

  **a.** Infrared rays

  **b.** Ultraviolet rays

  **c.** Visible light

  **d.** X rays

**20.** Why can't we see radio waves?

  **a.** They are sound waves.

  **b.** They don't have their own energy.

  **c.** Their frequency is too high.

  **d.** Their frequency is too low.

**21.** Which color of light has the longest wavelength and lowest frequency?

  **a.** Red

  **b.** Violet

  **c.** Green

  **d.** Black

**Writing**

Write a paragraph comparing and contrasting sound waves and light waves. Include information you find interesting about these waves. Make sure your paragraph has a beginning, a middle, and an end.

Copyright © 2006 Pearson Education, Inc. Duplication for classroom use is permitted

# Tests Answer Key

## Getting Started: Introduction Test

| | |
|---|---|
| 1. a | 11. a |
| 2. c | 12. b |
| 3. b | 13. c |
| 4. d | 14. c |
| 5. b | 15. d |
| 6. a | 16. a |
| 7. c | 17. c |
| 8. d | 18. d |
| 9. d | 19. b |
| 10. b | 20. a |

## Unit 1: Lesson 1 Test

| | |
|---|---|
| 1. b | 7. d |
| 2. d | 8. b |
| 3. c | 9. c |
| 4. a | 10. a |
| 5. b | 11. d |
| 6. c | |

### Writing
See Scoring Rubric on page 186.

## Unit 1: Lesson 2 Test

| | |
|---|---|
| 1. c | 7. a |
| 2. a | 8. d |
| 3. d | 9. b |
| 4. a | 10. d |
| 5. b | 11. c |
| 6. c | |

### Writing
See Scoring Rubric on page 186.

## Unit 1: Unit Test

| | |
|---|---|
| 1. a | 12. c |
| 2. c | 13. a |
| 3. b | 14. b |
| 4. b | 15. a |
| 5. d | 16. c |
| 6. a | 17. c |
| 7. d | 18. d |
| 8. a | 19. b |
| 9. b | 20. d |
| 10. d | 21. b |
| 11. d | |

### Writing
See Scoring Rubric on page 186.

## Unit 2: Lesson 1 Test

| | |
|---|---|
| 1. d | 7. b |
| 2. c | 8. a |
| 3. b | 9. c |
| 4. c | 10. b |
| 5. b | 11. d |
| 6. d | |

### Writing
See Scoring Rubric on page 186.

## Unit 2: Lesson 2 Test

| | |
|---|---|
| 1. c | 7. d |
| 2. d | 8. c |
| 3. c | 9. b |
| 4. a | 10. a |
| 5. d | 11. d |
| 6. b | |

### Writing
See Scoring Rubric on page 186.

## Unit 2: Unit Test

| | |
|---|---|
| 1. b | 12. b |
| 2. a | 13. b |
| 3. c | 14. d |
| 4. d | 15. c |
| 5. a | 16. c |
| 6. b | 17. b |
| 7. d | 18. c |
| 8. c | 19. d |
| 9. d | 20. a |
| 10. c | 21. c |
| 11. c | |

### Writing
See Scoring Rubric on page 186.

## Unit 3: Lesson 1 Test

| | |
|---|---|
| 1. c | 7. a |
| 2. b | 8. b |
| 3. d | 9. c |
| 4. c | 10. a |
| 5. c | 11. c |
| 6. d | |

### Writing
See Scoring Rubric on page 186.

## Unit 3: Lesson 2 Test

| | |
|---|---|
| 1. c | 7. a |
| 2. b | 8. d |
| 3. c | 9. b |
| 4. a | 10. c |
| 5. d | 11. c |
| 6. d | |

### Writing
See Scoring Rubric on page 186.

## Unit 3: Unit Test

| | |
|---|---|
| 1. a | 12. b |
| 2. c | 13. d |
| 3. b | 14. c |
| 4. c | 15. d |
| 5. a | 16. b |
| 6. a | 17. c |
| 7. d | 18. d |
| 8. c | 19. b |
| 9. b | 20. c |
| 10. d | 21. c |
| 11. a | |

### Writing
See Scoring Rubric on page 186.

## Unit 4: Lesson 1 Test

| | |
|---|---|
| 1. a | 7. b |
| 2. c | 8. a |
| 3. b | 9. b |
| 4. c | 10. c |
| 5. a | 11. d |
| 6. d | |

### Writing
See Scoring Rubric on page 186.

## Unit 4: Lesson 2 Test

| | |
|---|---|
| 1. d | 7. b |
| 2. a | 8. d |
| 3. c | 9. d |
| 4. d | 10. c |
| 5. b | 11. c |
| 6. d | |

### Writing
See Scoring Rubric on page 186.

## Unit 4: Unit Test

| | |
|---|---|
| 1. c | 12. d |
| 2. a | 13. b |
| 3. d | 14. c |
| 4. c | 15. c |
| 5. b | 16. a |
| 6. d | 17. b |
| 7. c | 18. c |
| 8. b | 19. a |
| 9. a | 20. d |
| 10. b | 21. b |
| 11. d | |

**Writing**

See Scoring Rubric on page 186.

## Unit 5: Lesson 1 Test

| | |
|---|---|
| 1. d | 7. a |
| 2. c | 8. c |
| 3. b | 9. b |
| 4. b | 10. a |
| 5. c | 11. b |
| 6. d | |

**Writing**

See Scoring Rubric on page 186.

## Unit 5: Lesson 2 Test

| | |
|---|---|
| 1. b | 7. d |
| 2. c | 8. a |
| 3. d | 9. b |
| 4. a | 10. d |
| 5. a | 11. b |
| 6. c | |

**Writing**

See Scoring Rubric on page 186.

## Unit 5: Unit Test

| | |
|---|---|
| 1. b | 12. d |
| 2. a | 13. b |
| 3. c | 14. c |
| 4. d | 15. a |
| 5. c | 16. b |
| 6. a | 17. d |
| 7. c | 18. a |
| 8. b | 19. b |
| 9. a | 20. d |
| 10. b | 21. b |
| 11. c | |

**Writing**

See Scoring Rubric on page 186.

## Unit 6: Lesson 1 Test

| | |
|---|---|
| 1. d | 7. c |
| 2. c | 8. b |
| 3. b | 9. c |
| 4. b | 10. d |
| 5. a | 11. a |
| 6. d | |

**Writing**

See Scoring Rubric on page 186.

## Unit 6: Lesson 2 Test

| | |
|---|---|
| 1. d | 7. b |
| 2. c | 8. a |
| 3. b | 9. d |
| 4. b | 10. d |
| 5. c | 11. a |
| 6. d | |

**Writing**

See Scoring Rubric on page 186.

## Unit 6: Unit Test

| | |
|---|---|
| 1. a | 12. b |
| 2. b | 13. c |
| 3. c | 14. c |
| 4. d | 15. d |
| 5. a | 16. d |
| 6. c | 17. b |
| 7. b | 18. d |
| 8. d | 19. c |
| 9. c | 20. d |
| 10. c | 21. a |
| 11. a | |

**Writing**

See Scoring Rubric on page 186.

# Credits

187 top, Gail Shumway/Taxi/Getty Images; 187 bottom, Mark Green/Taxi/Getty Images; 188 top, Andre Maslennikov/age fotostock america; 188 bottom, Andy Crawford/Dorling Kindersley; 189 top, Courtesy of Ohaus Corporation; 189 top middle, W. Geiersperger/Bettmann/CORBIS; 189 middle bottom, Tony Freeman/PhotoEdit; 189 bottom, Jacob Halaska/Index Stock Imagery; 190, Laurie O'Keefe/Pearson Education/Prentice Hall College Division; 191, © Nigel Cattlin/H.S.I./Photo Researchers, Inc.; 192, Andrew Butler/Dorling Kindersley; 193, Tom Leonard; 194, Runk/Schoenberger/Grant Heilman Photography, Inc.; 195, James Stevenson/Dorling Kindersley; 196, Matthew Ward/Dorling Kindersley; 197, Hans Pfletschinger/Peter Arnold, Inc.; 198, Tom Leonard; 199, Cary Wolinsky/Aurora; 200, © Digital Vision; 202, Getty Images; 203, Jochen Tack/Peter Arnold, Inc.; 204, Matt Meadows/Peter Arnold, Inc.; 205, Tim Davis/Photo Researchers, Inc.; 207, Dorling Kindersley; 208, Dinodia/Omni-Photo Communications, Inc.; 209 top, Washington State Tourism Development Division; 209 middle, InterNetwork Media/Photodisc/Getty Images; 209 bottom, Harry Glicken/David A. Johnston Cascades Volcano Observatory, Vancouver, WA/US Geological Survey/United States Department of the Interior; 210, David Parker/Science Photo Library/Photo Researchers, Inc.; 211, Harry Taylor/Dorling Kindersley; 212, Arnold Fisher/Photo Researchers, Inc.; 213, Robin Smith/photolibrary.com; 214, Peter Bull/Dorling Kindersley; 215, David A. Hardy/Photo Researchers, Inc.; 216, Aaron Horowitz/Bettmann/CORBIS; 217, NASA; 218, NASA; 219, Chris Butler/Photo Researchers, Inc.; 220, NASA; 221, Daniel Pyne/Dorling Kindersley; 222 left, John F. Kennedy Space Center/NASA; 222 middle, NASA; 222 right, NASA; 223, Naval Research Laboratory/U.S. Naval Historical Center (CuP) Photography; 224, Leslie Weidenman; 225, Morgan Cain & Associates; 226, Vanessa Davies/Dorling Kindersley; 227, Paul Morrell/Allstock/Getty Images; 228, Richard Walters/Visuals Unlimited; 229, John Mead/Science Photo Library/Photo Researchers, Inc.; 230, Richard Lewis/Dorling Kindersley; 232, Grant V. Faint/Image Bank/Getty Images; 233, Precision Graphics; 234, David Parker/Science Photo Library/Photo Researchers, Inc.; 235, © 1998 Richard Megna, Fundamental Photographs, NYC; 236, David Oliver/Taxi/Getty Images; 237, © Rex Interstock/Stock Connection; 238, Martucci Design.